Nuffield Primary Science
SCIENCE PROCESSES AND CONCEPT EXPLORATION

Electricity and magnetism

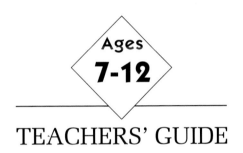

Ages
7-12

TEACHERS' GUIDE

PUBLISHED FOR THE NUFFIELD–CHELSEA CURRICULUM TRUST BY COLLINS EDUCATIONAL

NUFFIELD PRIMARY SCIENCE
Science Processes and Concept Exploration

Directors
Paul Black
Wynne Harlen

Deputy Director
Terry Russell

Project members
Robert Austin
Derek Bell
Adrian Hughes
Ken Longden
John Meadows
Linda McGuigan
Jonathan Osborne
Pamela Wadsworth
Dorothy Watt

First published 1993 by Collins Educational
An imprint of HarperCollins*Publishers*
77-85 Fulham Palace Road
London W6 8JB

Second edition published 1995
Reprinted 1996

ISBN 0 00 310254 8

Printed and bound in Hong Kong

Design by Carla Turchini, Chi Leung
Illustrations by John Booth, Gay Galsworthy,
Maureen Hallahan, Mary Lonsdale, Sally Neave,
Karen Tushingham, Jakki Wood
Cover artwork by Karen Tushingham

Photograph acknowledgements
Page 40: Science Photo Picture Library

Commissioned photography by Oliver Hatch

The Trust and the Publishers would like to thank the
governors, staff and pupils of Hillbrook Primary School,
Tooting, for their kind co-operation with many of the
photographs in this book.

Safety adviser
Peter Borrows

Other contributors
Elizabeth Harris
Carol Joyes
Anne de Normanville
Ralph Hancock

Contents

Explanation of symbols in the margins

 Warning

 Good opportunities to develop and assess work related to Experimental and Investigative Science

 Notes which may be useful to the teacher

 Vocabulary work

 Opportunities for children to use information technology

 Equipment needed

 Reference to the pupils' books

CHAPTER 1

Introduction

1.1 The SPACE approach to teaching and learning science

A primary class where the SPACE approach to science is being used may not at first seem different from any other class engaged in science activities; in either, children will be mentally and physically involved in exploring objects and events in the world around them. However, a closer look will reveal that both the children's activities and the teacher's role differ from those found in other approaches. The children are not following instructions given by others; they are not solving a problem set them by someone else. They are deeply involved in work which is based on their own ideas, and they have taken part in deciding how to do it.

The teacher has, of course, prepared carefully to reach the point where children try out their ideas. She or he will have started on the topic by giving children opportunities to explore from their own experience situations which embody important scientific ideas. The teacher will have ensured that the children have expressed their ideas about what they are exploring, using one or more of a range of approaches – from whole class discussion to talking with individual children, or asking children to write or draw – and will have explored the children's reasons for having those ideas.

With this information the teacher will have decided how to help the children to develop or revise their ideas. That may involve getting the children to use the ideas to make a prediction, then testing it by seeing if it works in practice; or the children may gather further evidence to discuss and think about. In particular, the teacher will note how 'scientific' children have been in their gathering and use of evidence; and should, by careful questioning, encourage greater rigour in the use of scientific process skills.

It is essential that the children change their ideas only as a result of what they find themselves, not by merely accepting ideas which they are told are better.

By carefully exploring children's ideas, taking them seriously and choosing appropriate ways of helping the children to test them, the teacher can move children towards ideas which apply more widely and fit the evidence better – those which are, in short, more scientific.

You will find more information about the SPACE approach in the Nuffield Primary Science *Science Co-ordinators' handbook.*

1.2 Useful strategies

Finding out children's ideas

This guide points out many opportunities for finding out children's ideas. One way is simply by talking, but there are many others. We have found the following strategies effective. How you use them may depend on the area of science you are dealing with. In Chapter 3 you will find examples of these strategies. More information about them is given in the *Science Co-ordinators' handbook*.

Talking and open questioning

Whole class discussions can be useful for sharing ideas, but they do not always give all children a chance to speak. It is often helpful if children are allowed to think of their own ideas first, perhaps working them out in drawings, and are then encouraged to share these with others – perhaps with just one other child, or with a larger group.

Annotated drawings

Asking children to draw their ideas can give a particularly clear insight into what they think. It also gives you a chance to discuss the children's ideas with them. Words conveying these ideas can then be added to the drawing, either by you or by the child. Such work can be kept as a permanent record.

Sorting and classifying

This can be a useful way of helping children to clarify their ideas and to record their thinking. They could sort a collection of objects or pictures into groups.

Writing down ideas

Children may instead write down their responses to questions you pose. Writing gives children the opportunity to express their own views, which can then be shared with others or investigated further.

Log books and diaries

These can be used to record changes over a longer investigation. They need not necessarily be kept by individual children, but could be kept by a whole group or class. Children can jot down their ideas, as words or drawings, when they notice changes, recording their reasons for what they observe.

Helping children to develop their ideas

Letting children test their own ideas

This will involve children in using some or all of the process skills of science:

- observing
- measuring
- hypothesizing
- predicting
- planning and carrying out fair tests
- interpreting results and findings
- communicating

It is an important strategy which can, and should, be used often. The *use* of process skills *develops* them – for example, through greater attention to detail in observing, more careful control of variables in fair tests, and taking all the evidence into account in interpreting the results.

Encouraging generalization from one context to another

Does an explanation proposed for a particular event fit one which is not exactly the same, but which involves the same scientific concept? You or the children might suggest other contexts that might be tried. This might be done by discussing the evidence for and against the explanation, or by gathering more evidence and testing the idea in the other context, depending on children's familiarity with the events being examined.

Discussing the words children use to describe their ideas

Children can be asked to be quite specific about the meaning of words they use, whether scientific or not. They can be prompted to think of alternative words which have almost the same meaning. They can discuss, where appropriate, words which have special meaning in a scientific context, and so be helped to realize the difference between the 'everyday' use of some words and the scientific one.

Extending the range of evidence

Some of the children's ideas may be consistent with the evidence at present available to them, but could be challenged by extending the range of evidence. This applies particularly to things which are not easily observed, such as slow changes; or those which are normally hidden, such as the insides of objects. Attempts to make these imperceptible things perceptible, often by using secondary sources, help children to consider a wider range of evidence.

Getting children to communicate their ideas

Expressing ideas in any way – through writing, drawing, modelling or, particularly, through discussion – involves thinking them through, and often rethinking and revising them. Discussion has a further advantage in that it is two-way and children can set others' ideas against their own. Just realizing that there are different ideas helps them to reconsider their own.

1.3 Equal opportunities

The SPACE approach to teaching and learning science gives opportunities for every child to build on and develop his or her experiences, skills and ideas. It can therefore be used to benefit pupils of all kinds and at any stage of development. This is fully discussed in the *Science Co-ordinators' handbook.*

1.4 Electricity and magnetism and the curriculum

This teachers' guide is divided into four themes; in each one there is a section on finding out children's ideas, examples of ideas children have, and a section on helping children to develop their ideas.

Nuffield Primary Science Themes

Sources and uses of electricity

This theme indicates ways in which children might develop their ideas about the sources of electricity and everyday uses of it.

Many children appear to associate electricity with the mains supply rather than batteries. They may not know that electricity is generated in power stations; instead, they may think it comes from lighting, or from under the ground. Children often think of electricity causing heating effects and that all forms of electricity are dangerous.

Activities are suggested in which children can become more familiar with the different types of battery we use, investigate the effect of batteries in simple circuits and the generation of electricity by a dynamo, and find out about power stations through the use of secondary sources.

This theme may be helpful in preparing children for work on simple electric circuits.

Circuits

This theme indicates ways in which children might develop their ideas about simple circuits.

Many children do not know that certain materials conduct electricity. They may be unaware that electrical components and electrical sources need two connections. Once children have successfully connected a component into a circuit, they may still have difficulty in generalizing about the connection of any component in a circuit.

Activities are suggested which should help children to develop their ideas about electrical conductors, connecting electrical components, and constructing various types of circuit. In all of these activities children will have many opportunities to develop the idea of a complete electrical circuit.

Altering the flow of electricity

This theme indicates ways in which children's ideas about switches and controlling the flow of electricity might be developed.

Although children may be familiar with switches used in everyday electrical appliances, they may not be aware that a switch completes and breaks a circuit and provides a means of controlling the appliance.

In the activities suggested, children can design and make their own switching systems, find out about the different types of switch used in everyday electrical appliances, and design and make alarm systems and simple electrical games. Children can be introduced to the use of a computer and logic gates to control electricity.

Throughout the theme children will have opportunities to develop further their ideas on the uses of electricity and the construction of circuits.

Magnets

This theme indicates ways in which children's ideas about magnets might be developed.

Some children think that all magnets are horseshoe-shaped and that magnets attract any type of metal. They may explain the action of magnets in terms of 'glue' or think of magnets as having magical properties.

In the activities suggested, children can investigate magnetic and non-magnetic materials, forces between magnets, electromagnets and the use of magnets in compasses. There are opportunities for children to design and make their own magnetic games and to investigate the ways in which magnets are used in the home and elsewhere.

National Curriculum Programmes of Study	Environmental Studies 5-14 (Scotland): Science
Physical Processes **1 Electricity** **a** that a complete circuit, including a battery or power supply, is needed to make electrical devices work.	**Understanding Energy and Forces (Stages P4 to P6)** **Forms and sources of energy** • electricity as a form of energy; • sources of electrical energy.
Physical Processes **1 Electricity** **d** how to represent series circuits by drawings and diagrams, and how to construct series circuits on the basis of drawings and diagrams. **Materials and their Properties** **1 Grouping and classifying materials** **c** that some materials are better electrical conductors than others.	**Understanding Energy and Forces (Stages P4 to P6)** **Properties and uses of energy** • construction of battery operated circuits to operate a range of mechanisms; • electrical conductors and insulators; • electrical safety.
Physical Processes **1 Electricity** **b** how switches can be used to control electrical devices; **c** ways of varying the current in a circuit to make bulbs brighter or dimmer.	**Understanding Energy and Forces (Stages P4 to P6)** **Properties and uses of energy** • construction of battery operated circuits; • electrical conductors and insulators; • electrical safety.
Physical Processes **2 Forces and motion** **a** that there are forces of attraction and repulsion between magnets, and forces of attraction between magnets and magnetic materials. **Materials and their properties** **1 Grouping and classifying materials** **a** to compare everyday materials on the basis of their properties, including hardness, strength, flexibility and magnetic behaviour, and to relate these properties to everyday uses of the materials.	

1.5 Experimental and Investigative Science

Two important aspects of children's learning in science are:

◆ learning how to investigate the world around them;
◆ learning to make sense of the world around them using scientific ideas.

These are reflected in the National Curriculum. 'Experimental and Investigative Science' covers the first aspect. The second aspect is covered by the rest of the Programme of Study. Although these two aspects of science learning are separated in the National Curriculum they cannot be separated in practice and it is not useful to try to do so. Through investigation children explore their ideas and/or test out the ideas which arise from discussion. As a result, ideas may be advanced, but this will depend on the children's investigation skills. Thus it is important to develop these skills in the context of activities which extend ideas. So there is no separate Nuffield Primary Science teachers' guide on scientific investigations, because opportunities to make these occur throughout all the guides and they form an essential part of the SPACE approach.

Thus in this guide you will find investigations which provide opportunities to develop and assess the skills and understanding set out in Experimental and Investigative Science. These are marked in the text by the symbol shown here. In this teachers' guide, the investigations which cover the most skills are 'Simple circuits with lightbulbs: Lighting a bulb' (page 47), 'Insulators and conductors: Testing materials' (page 54) and 'Using magnets to find direction' (page 77).

It is important that teachers give active guidance to pupils during investigations to help them work out how to improve the way in which they plan and carry out their investigations.

Experimental and Investigative Science is about the ways scientific evidence can be obtained, about the ways observations and measurements are made, and about the way in which the evidence is analysed. It therefore sets out three main ways in which pupils can develop their ability to do experimental and investigative science, as follows:-

1   'Planning experimental work'. Here, children should be helped to make progress from asking general and vague questions, to suggesting ideas which could be tested. Teachers' discussion with pupils should aim to help them to make predictions, using their existing understanding, on the basis of which they can decide what evidence should be collected. This should lead them to think about what apparatus and equipment they should use.

When children describe plans for their work, they should be helped to think about what features they are going to change, what effects of these changes they are going to observe or measure, and what features they must keep the same. In this way they can come to understand what is meant by 'a fair test'.

2 'Obtaining evidence'. Children should make observations in the light of their ideas about what they are looking for and why. When they describe their observations, teachers may have to help them to improve, for example by reminding them of their original aims and plan for the work. Such help should also encourage progress from qualitative comparisons and judgements to appreciating the value of making quantitative measurements (for example 'cold water' is qualitative, 'water at 12°C' is quantitative). This should lead to the development of skills with a variety of instruments and to increasing care and accuracy in measurement, involving, for example, repeating measurements to check.

3 'Considering evidence'. Here, children should first learn to record their evidence in systematic and clear ways, starting with simple drawings and then learning to use tables, bar charts and line graphs to display the patterns in numerical data. Then they should be asked to think about and discuss their results, considering what might be learnt from any trends or patterns. As ideas develop, they should be careful in checking their evidence against the original idea underlying the investigation and should become increasingly critical in discussing alternative explanations which might fit their evidence. In such discussions, they should be helped to relate their arguments to their developing scientific understanding. They should also be guided to see possibilities for conducting their investigation more carefully, or in quite different ways.

Whilst these three may seem to form a natural sequence of stages, children's work might not follow this particular sequence. For example, some might start with evidence from their observations and proceed on this basis to propose a hypothesis and a plan to test it. For others, the results of one task may be the starting point for a new inquiry involving new measurements. Useful learning about how to investigate might arise when only one or two of the above aspects of an investigation are involved, or when the teacher tells children about some aspects so that they can concentrate on others. However, there should be some occasions for all pupils when they carry out the whole process of investigation by themselves.

The assessment examples given in chapter 4 are analysed in relation to the level descriptions, which describe children's progress in relation to these three aspects: *planning experimental work, obtaining evidence* and *considering evidence*. Thus, these three provide a framework both for guiding children and for assessing their progress in experimental and investigative work.

CHAPTER 2

Planning

2.1 Introduction: planning with children's ideas in mind

The key scientific ideas presented in this guide can be explored in various contexts, and many of the suggested activities can be incorporated into cross-curricular topic work. This chapter uses a worked example as an aid to planning a topic. Further information on planning is given in the *Science Co-ordinators' handbook.*

A teacher using the SPACE approach should take into account:

◆ the need to find out children's own ideas, not only at the beginning of the work but also at intervals during it;
◆ the importance of planning the investigations with the children, using their ideas as the starting point;
◆ the concepts that are being explored;
◆ the direction in which the children's ideas are developing.

2.2 Cross-curricular topics

Activities which explore the ideas covered in this teachers' guide to *Electricity and magnetism* may be approached via a number of topics in addition to the one set out as an example in the planning sheets (pages 15–16). It is assumed that teachers will adapt the topic to whatever local resources are of interest and readily to hand. Some possibilities are given below.

Safety

Children could find out about safety in the home, at school and in their neighbourhood. How do we keep ourselves safe? Who helps us to keep safe? How do we use sounds, colour and reflection of light to warn people of danger?
What are the safe forms of electricity?
What devices keep us safe from fires and burglars?
Children could devise their own warning and safety devices; these devices could incorporate switches, sensors and logic gates in circuits. Children could talk to people in public services concerned with health and safety. They could find out more about aspects of safety in transport. Why do we need to wear a safety belt? How do we stop things moving? What keeps us safe on a bicycle? How do we warn and communicate with ships and aeroplanes? How do we rescue people at sea? How did these rescue services develop?
They could design a road sign.

Some links with other Nuffield Primary Science teachers' guides and pupils' books include:

Light – designing warning lights, comparing materials and colours in safety clothing;
Living processes – keeping healthy;
Forces and movement – stopping things moving, floating and sinking;
Sound and music – designing devices to give warnings.

Homes

Children could find out about the different types of buildings, places and uses we have for homes – homes for people who move from place to place, holiday homes, family homes, homes on water, homes in the town and country.
How have our homes changed: what is different about modern homes compared with those in the past?
What were the reasons for building castles and manor houses?
What materials are used to build homes?
Children could find out about the domestic appliances and fuels needed for running a home. Where does the water, gas and electricity come from, and how do we pay for them?
Children could design their own room or make a model home: what materials would be best for making the curtains, floor covering, roof, walls or carpets?

Some links with other Nuffield Primary Science teachers' guides and pupils' books include:

Light – light sources;
Materials – natural and manufactured materials used for building houses, their properties and uses;
Using energy – energy sources;
Sound and music – insulation.

Toys and games

At the beginning of the topic, children could bring into school toys that have some means of propulsion or have to be pushed. The different means of propulsion could be compared. Toys that move through the air, on the ground or in water could all be included. Those toys in which the mechanisms are obvious and accessible will be most useful. In some electrical devices the mechanisms cannot be observed and are difficult to describe simply. Devices such as cotton reels, cars, elastic driven aircraft (catapulted or with propellers), and helicopters which can be launched by pulling a length of string (as with a spinning top) are all useful in showing propulsion mechanisms.
Children could design and make their own toys and models and incorporate electrical motors into their designs. They may wish to use a computer to control a toy car so that it goes forwards and backwards. Young children may be interested to find out about traditional and popular team and individual games. They can devise a variety of their own games.
Children could invent board games based on magnetic attraction and repulsion, or electrical games in which a circuit has to be completed to score or to select a question. Ball bearings could be used to complete circuits in which buzzers or bells act as signals.

Some links with other Nuffield Primary Science teachers' guides and pupils' books include:

Using energy – mechanisms for making toys move;
Forces and movement – making toys move, and slowing them down;
Materials – what are the toys made of?

2.3 Topic plan examples

The following plans illustrate how the science related to *Electricity and magnetism* may be embedded in a cross-curricular topic. The topic presented is 'Safety' and opportunities for exploring mathematics, language, history, geography, design technology and art have been indicated on the first plan. On the second plan the science work has been amplified to illustrate possible areas of exploration based within the overall topic. It is important to remember these are only examples and are not intended to be exhaustive.

2.4 Use of information technology

Specific examples of opportunities to use information technology are indicated by this symbol in the margin and referred to in the text. The examples include:

◆ word processing to produce reports of investigations;
◆ simple databases to record and analyse data collected;
◆ use of appropriate software to control working models;
◆ tape recorders for reporting investigations.

2.5 Pupils' books

The pupils' books accompanying this guide are called *Electricity and Magnetism* for the lower juniors and *More About Electricity and Magnetism* for the upper juniors. The pupils' books are intended to be used spread by spread. The spreads are not sequential, and they are covered in these notes in thematic order.

Features of the pupils' books include:
◆ Stimulus spreads, often visual, designed to raise questions, arouse curiosity, and to promote discussion.

◆ Information spreads, which give secondary source material in a clear and attractive way.

◆ Activity ideas, to form the basis of investigations to be carried out by the children.

◆ Cross-curricular spreads and stories which can act as a basis for creative writing, or spreads with a historical or creative focus.

◆ Real life examples of applications of science in the everyday world.

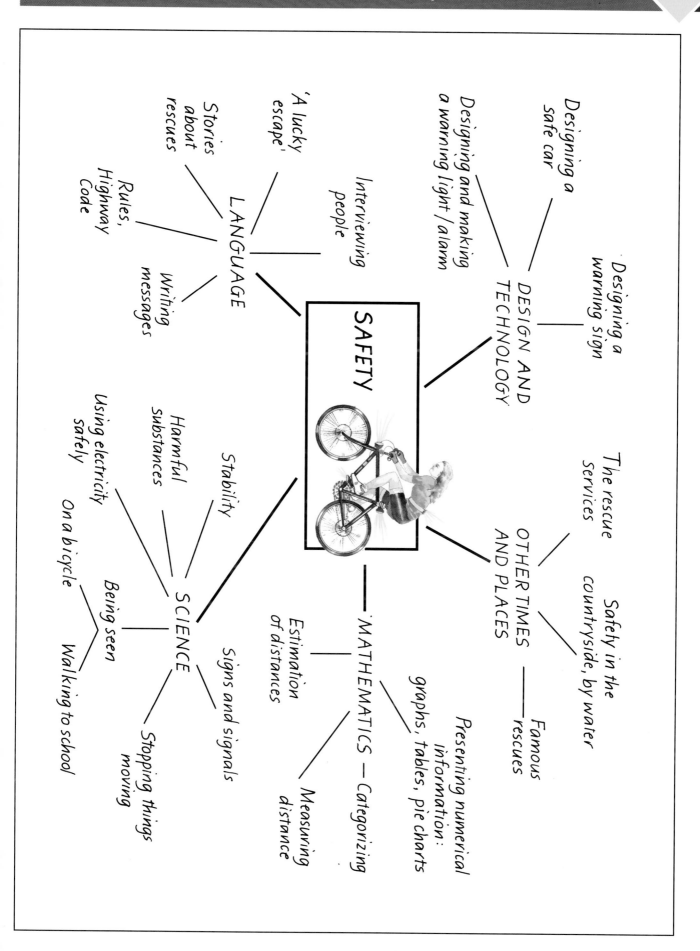

SAFETY

DESIGN AND TECHNOLOGY
- Designing a safe car
- Designing and making a warning light / alarm
- Designing a warning sign

LANGUAGE
- 'A lucky escape'
- Stories about rescues
- Rules, Highway Code
- Writing messages
- Interviewing people

OTHER TIMES AND PLACES
- The rescue services
- Safety in the countryside, by water
- Famous rescues

SCIENCE
- Stability
- Harmful substances
- Using electricity safely
- Being seen
- On a bicycle
- Walking to school
- Signs and signals
- Stopping things moving

MATHEMATICS — Categorizing
- Estimation of distances
- Measuring distance
- Presenting numerical information: graphs, tables, pie charts

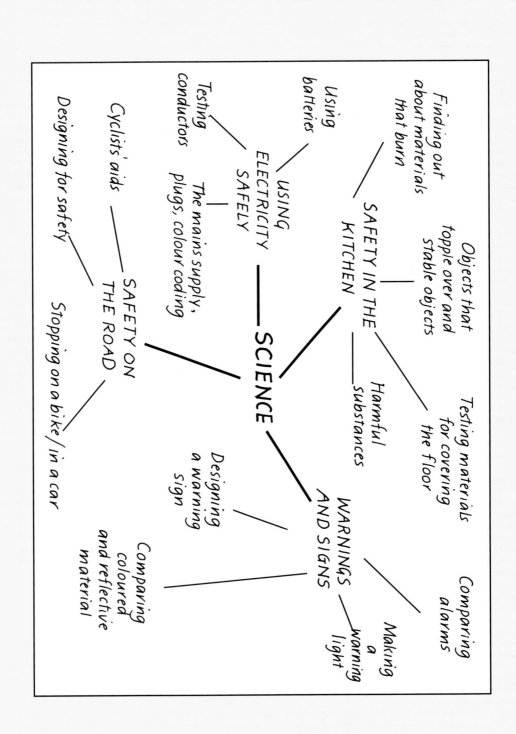

SCIENCE

SAFETY IN THE KITCHEN

Finding out about materials that burn

Objects that topple over and stable objects

Testing materials for covering the floor

Harmful substances

USING ELECTRICITY SAFELY

Using batteries

Testing conductors

The mains supply, plugs, colour coding

SAFETY ON THE ROAD

Cyclists' aids

Designing for safety

Stopping on a bike / in a car

WARNINGS AND SIGNS

Designing a warning sign

Comparing coloured and reflective material

Making a warning light

Comparing alarms

Electricity and magnetism

Currents pages 2–3

Purpose: To help children think about electric currents and the way electricity is used to power appliances.
Note: An electrical current is not like the current in a river, but it may be a useful comparison and a good way of introducing an electrical current.
Questions for discussion: What do you think a current is? What is an electric current?
Teachers' guide cross-references: *Electricity and magnetism*, page 31, 49.

Amber, shocks, and one-eyed giants pages 4–5

Purpose: To discuss the natural forms of electricity children may have noticed, such as lightning.
Notes: The spread introduces a Greek myth. Lightning is natural static electricity caused by drops of water in clouds moving up and down, eventually causing sparking – like the sparks you sometimes get when you take off a jumper. This heats the air, which very quickly expands and then cools and contracts, causing the noise of thunder.
Extension activity: Children could write their own imaginative stories about the cause of thunder and lightning.
Teachers' guide cross-references: *Electricity and magnetism*, pages 89–93.

Underground connections pages 8–9

Purpose: To help children think about mains electricity and how it travels from power stations to our homes; to examine the difference between mains and battery electricity.
Questions for discussion: What are the two ways in which we get electricity? What are the advantages and disadvantages of each source of electricity? (Batteries are expensive, often cumbersome and run out; mains electricity can be dangerous.) What happens when there is no electricity?
Teachers' guide cross-references: *Electricity and magnetism*, pages 13, 30, 90–91.

Electricity at the shopping centre pages 12–13

Purpose: To act as a quiz page.
Note: All answers except the first one are found in the word search, as is the name of the photographer.
Extension activities: The class could list all the different uses of electricity shown on the spread.
Teachers' guide cross-reference: *Electricity and magnetism*, page 39.

Vibrations pages 14–15

Purpose: To explain the role of electricity in sound amplification and recording.
Extension activities: Follow up the idea that voices make vibrations, too. Try an experiment where children record their voices using a tape recorder laid flat. Put a tray containing a fine layer of sand on top of it and play the voices back. The sand arranges itself according to the different sound patterns made by the voices.

Pupils' book cross-references: More about sound and music, pages 20–23.

Electricity from batteries or the mains? pages 16–17

Purpose: To look at the advantages and disadvantages of different sources of electricity.
Question for discussion: What are the sources of electricity shown?
Teachers' guide cross-references: Electricity and magnetism, pages 35–39.

Electricity going places pages 18–19

Purpose: To provide information about the different ways in which transport can be powered, showing examples of ways in which electricity is used in daily life.
Notes: A car's battery is used to start the engine, not to power its motion. Battery-powered cars cannot go very fast, and the batteries need regular recharging. The forms of transport on page 19 are supplied with a constant flow of electricity from overhead sources (an extra rail is an alternative). Electrically powered vehicles are not pollution-free – generating electricity can involve the use of fossil fuels.
Extension activities: The class could try making their own electrically powered buggy using a battery – a design and technology link.
Teachers' guide cross-references: Electricity and magnetism, page 49.

Worrying with Uncle Harry pages 10–11

Purpose: To show that electricity can be dangerous, and that there are safety measures we should take when we use it in the home.
Notes: In addition to poor cables and connections, Uncle Harry should also worry about mixing electricity and water. This is why we have a different kind of light switch in the bathroom from other rooms.
Extension activities: Children could look inside a plug – but they should take care. They could discuss what their parents or carers tell them about electricity and its dangers.
Teachers' guide cross-references: Electricity and magnetism, pages 12, 15–16, 51–2, 54, 92–94.

Electrical you pages 20–21

Purpose: A 'wow' information spread, which explains that the nervous system uses weak electrical currents (that is, humans run on electricity).
Pupils' book cross-references: Living things in action pages 10-11.
Teachers' guide cross-references: Electricity and magnetism, pages 55, 92-3; *Living processes,* page 14.

The mystery rock pages 6–7

Purpose: To provide secondary source material about the discovery of magnets.
Extension activity: Conduct the experiments described in the teachers' guide, and ask the class to describe what happens when they suspend a magnet.
Pupils' book cross-references: More about time and space, pages 10-11.
Teachers' guide cross-references: Electricity and magnetism, page 72, 75, 77.

Treasure map pages 22–23

Purpose: A starting point for using a compass for orienteering, and to introduce the use of magnets in a compass.
Notes: Read the co-ordinates along the base first, and then the vertical ones.
Extension activities: The map could be copied and mounted on card so that children can use the map to find their own treasure (a small iron or steel object stuck underneath it). Following directions using co-ordinates, other children can try to find the treasure. They can test the result by using a compass or a small magnet. These will be attracted to the metal.
Teachers' guide cross-references: Electricity and magnetism, pages 77, 97-8.

More about electricity and magnetism

Measuring electricity pages 2–3

Purpose: To show children how electricity is measured.
Note: Canada and Norway have long dark winters so they need more heat and light. There is plenty of hydro-electric power in both countries, so electricity is cheap there.
Extension activity: Children could count the number of light bulbs they have at home.
Teachers' guide cross-reference: Electricity and magnetism, page 13.

Batteries pages 4–5

Purpose: To give children information about the use of batteries.
Question for discussion: What information is given on batteries, and what does it mean? (Strength of battery, the positive and negative signs.)
Extension activities: The children could look inside a torch (the simpler the better) to see how the circuit is made. They could look at different kinds of batteries.
Teachers' guide cross-references: Electricity and magnetism, pages 13, 35–9.

Discovering electricity pages 6–7

Purpose: A historical spread, to tell children the story of the discovery of electricity.
Extension activity: Take the class to a museum to look at early electrical appliances.
Teachers' guide cross-references: Electricity and magnetism, 38–9.

Electrical lifesaver pages 8–9

Purpose: To make the point that lightning is dangerous (most people die if they are hit by it) but that controlled electric shocks can be used in medicine.
Notes: Discuss with the children what they should do in an emergency like this. (Normally, they should get help immediately.)
Extension activity: Children could write their own stories about medical emergencies.
Teachers' guide cross-references: Electricity and magnetism, pages 12, 15–16.

Brenda's day pages 12–13

Purpose: To discuss the different ways electricity is used in a school and the different ways in which people use electricity.
Extension activity: The children could interview the school caretaker or cook and write the story of their day and how they use electricity in their work.
Teachers' guide cross-references: Electricity and magnetism, pages 13, 39.

The story of Michael Faraday pages 14–15

Purpose: A story spread to tell children about the life and work of Michael Faraday.
Notes: The tallest man in the middle of the front row, opposite Michael Faraday, is Prince Albert, husband of Queen Victoria.
Extension activities: The children could make books about science experiments. You could arrange for the class to attend one of the Royal Institution's Christmas lectures for children – still held in the same lecture theatre that Michael Faraday used.

Where does mains electricity come from? pages 16–17

Purpose: To help children develop their ideas about the different ways of generating electricity.
Extension activities: Ask the children to write about three ways that electricity is produced: the three shown here are coal-fired, nuclear and hydro-electric (water-powered). Using information from this and the next spread, children could do a role play about a power station being built, acting the parts of those who want to build and those, such as local residents, who might not approve. Children could discuss the advantages and disadvantages of each type of power station.
Pupils' book cross-references: More about using energy pages 12-19.
Teachers' guide cross-references: Electricity and magnetism, pages 38-9, 96-7; *Using energy,* pages 13, 63-4.

Electricity and pollution pages 18–19

Purpose: To help the children think about the environmental problems associated with the various ways of generating electricity.
Extension activities: as for pages 16–17.
Teachers' guide cross-references: Electricity and magnetism, pages 38-9, 96-7; *Using energy,* pages 13, 63-4.

Lighting a television studio pages 20–21

Purpose: To provide an interesting context for a discussion of uses of electricity.
Extension activities: Children could look at the lighting equipment used on a school stage.

Clues to life before electricity pages 22–23

Purpose: To help children envisage a world without electricity.
Extension activities: Using the example of food preservation, ask the children to list the differences in the ways milk, for example, used to be preserved (before electricity) and the ways it is preserved now. Children could try making butter or yoghurt from milk – a link with design and technology.
Teachers' guide cross-references: Electricity and magnetism, pages 13, 39.

They do it with magnets pages 10–11

Purpose: To help children develop ideas about the relationship between magnets and electricity, to show how a generator works to produce electricity, and how an electric motor works.
Extension activity: Children could sort out materials using a magnet and devise their own machine for extracting metal from a scrap heap – a link with design and technology.
Pupils' book cross-references: More about using energy pages 18-19.
Teachers' guide cross-references: Electricity and magnetism, pages 78-9, 97.

2.6 Planning your science programme in school

The following pages give examples of how two schools have planned their science programme for the whole of Key Stage 2. Planning of this kind helps to provide continuity and progression in children's learning in science. The development of such whole school programmes is discussed more fully in the *Science Co-ordinators' Handbook*.

Each plan covers the requirements for the National Curriculum at Key Stage 2 and shows which themes in the Nuffield Primary Science Teachers' Guides have been used for planning the topic in detail by the class teacher.

Example 1 (page 23)

Based in a semi-rural area this junior school has approximately 170 children on roll. There are no mixed age groups in the school. The plan provides for overlaps in order to provide opportunities for pupils to revisit concepts and build on their previous experience.

The overall curriculum is planned around topics which are history-led in the Autumn term, science-led in the Spring term and geography-led in the Summer term. Therefore, where ever possible cross-curricular links are developed, but if this becomes contrived, then subject specific mini-topics are planned. The programme only shows the Science elements taught each term.

Example 2 (page 24)

This urban school has recently reviewed its science programme in order to help encourage progression in the concepts covered and avoid repetition of the same activities. Teachers asked for guidance but also wanted the flexibility to develop the topics in a way which was appropriate to their own class.

It was also felt that some concepts, not necessarily demanded by the National Curriculum, should be covered e.g. Seasons. Therefore, suitable topics are included in the programme.

The summer term in Year 6 is free to accommodate SATs and to allow teachers time to further develop the interests of children.

Example 1

	AUTUMN TERM	SPRING TERM	SUMMER TERM
YEAR 3	The Earth and beyond/Magnetism	All about me	Service to our homes
Nuffield Primary Science Teachers' Guide	The Earth in Space 3.1, 3.2, 3.3 Electricity and magnetism 3.4	Living processes 3.1, 3.2, 3.3 The variety of life 3.2 Light 3.1	Electricity and magnetism 3.1, 3.2, 3.3 Materials 3.1 Using energy 3.2
Programme of Study †	Sc4:4a, b, c, d; Sc4:2a	Sc2: 1a; 2a, b, e, f; Sc4:3a, d	Sc3:1a, b, c; Sc4:1a, b, c
YEAR 4	Sound and music / Mechanisms	Habitats	Built environment
Nuffield Primary Science Teachers' Guide	Sound and music 3.1, 3.2 Using energy 3.3	The variety of life 3.1 Living processes 3.4 Living things in their environment 3.1, 3.2	Materials 3.2, 3.3 Using energy 3.1
Programme of Study †	Sc4:3e, f, g; Sc4:2d, e	Sc2:1b; 3a, b, c, d; 4a; Sc3:1d	Sc3:1e; 2a, b, c, d
YEAR 5	Electricity/Starting and stopping	Structures	Earth and atmosphere/ Light
Nuffield Primary Science Teachers' Guide	Electricity and magnetism 3.2, 3.3 Forces and movement 3.1, 3.2	Materials 3.1, 3.2, 3.3 Rocks, soil and weather 3.1 The variety of life 3.3	Rocks, soil and weather 3.2 The Earth in Space 3.1, 3.2, 3.3, 3.4 Light 3.2, 3.3
Programme of Study †	Sc4:1a, b, c, d; Sc4:2b, c	Sc3:1b, d; 2f; 3a, b, c, d, e	Sc3:2e; Sc4:4a, b, c, d; Sc4:3a, b, c
YEAR 6	The human body/Keeping healthy	Forces	Our environment
Nuffield Primary Science Teachers' Guide	Living processes 3.2, 3.3 The variety of life 3.2	Forces and movement 3.1, 3.2, 3.3, 3.4 Electricity and magnetism 3.4 Using energy 3.3	Living things in their environment 3.2, 3.3, 3.4
Programme of Study †	Sc2:2c, d, g, h	Sc4:2a, b, c, d, e, f, g, h	Sc2:5a, b, c, d, e

† For the purposes of these charts the references to sections of the Programme of Study have been abbreviated as follows:
Sc2 = Life Processes and Living Things
Sc3 = Materials and their Properties
Sc4 = Physical Processes

Example 2

	AUTUMN TERM		SPRING TERM		SUMMER TERM	
YEAR 3	Earth and time	Reflections and shadows	What's under our feet?	Moving things	Variety of life	Habitats
Nuffield Primary Science Teachers' Guide	The Earth in Space 3.1, 3.2	Light 3.2	Rocks, soil and weather 3.1 Living things in their environment 3.3	Forces and movement 3.1	The variety of life 3.1	Living things in their environment 3.1
Programme of Study †	Sc4:4a, b, c, d	Sc4:3a, b, c	Sc2:5e; Sc3:1d	Sc4:2a, b, c, d, e	Sc2:1a, b; 4a	Sc2:5a, b
YEAR 4	Frictional forces	Hot and cold	Materials and their properties	Sounds	Growing	Electricity
Nuffield Primary Science Teachers' Guide	Forces and movement 3.2	Using energy 3.1	Materials 3.1	Sound and music 3.1	Living processes 3.1, 3.4	Electricity and magnetism 3.1, 3.2, 3.3
Programme of Study †	Sc4:2b, c, f, g, h	Sc3:2b, c	Sc3:1a, b, e	Sc4:3e, f	Sc2:3a, b, c, d	Sc3:1c; Sc4:1a, b, c
YEAR 5	The Earth in the Solar System	Weather and its effects	Feeding relationships	Individual variation	Light sources	Sounds travelling
Nuffield Primary Science Teachers' Guides	The Earth in Space 3.1, 3.2, 3.3	Rocks, soil and weather 3.1, 3.2	Living things in their environment 3.2, 3.3	The variety of life 3.2	Light 3.1	Sound and music 3.2
Programme of Study †	Sc4:c, d	Sc3:1d, 2e	Sc2:5c, d, e	Sc2:4a; 5a	Sc4:3a, b, c, d	Sc4:3e, f, g
YEAR 6	Forces and movement	Living processes	Electricity	Materials		
Nuffield Primary Science Teachers' Guide	Forces and movement 3.3, 3.4	Living processes 3.2, 3.3	Electricity and magnetism 3.1, 3.2, 3.3	Materials 3.2, 3.3		
Programme of Study †	Sc4:2d, e, f, g, h	Sc2:2a, b, c, d, e, f, g, h	Sc4:1c, d	Sc3:2a, b, d, f; 3a, b, c, d, e		

2.7 Resources

Full use should be made of the school grounds or nearby open spaces.

The precise nature of the resources needed at any time will, of course, depend upon the ideas that the children have and the methods of testing that they devise. However, the following list provides a general guide to the resources needed to carry out the investigations shown in this book.

Magnets – a selection
Collection of common objects and materials to test for conductivity and magnetism
Wires, crocodile clips, bulb holders, buzzers, switches, motors, bulbs, batteries
Hand lenses
Car headlight bulbs
Computer control box
Corks, paper clips, drawing pins, drink cans, wood, dowel
Reference books.

2.8 Warnings

Activities which need particular care are indicated by this symbol in the margin. Everything possible should be done to ensure the safety of the children during their investigations. You should consult any guidelines on safety published by your own Local Education Authority and, if your school or LEA is a member, by CLEAPSS. See also the Association for Science Education publication *Be safe! Some aspects of safety in school science and technology for Key Stages 1 and 2* (2nd edition, 1990). This contains more detailed advice than can be included here.

The points listed below require particular attention.

Teach children never to misuse mains electricity, and warn them of electrical dangers in the home.

Children must never experiment with mains electricity. All investigations of circuits should be done using batteries.

Do not allow children to cut open batteries since their contents can be corrosive and poisonous.

Do not mix different types of battery in the same battery holder.

Never attempt to recharge batteries which are not intended to be recharged.

CHAPTER 3

Exploring electricity and magnetism

Theme organizer

ELECTRICITY AND MAGNETISM

SOURCES AND USES OF ELECTRICITY

3.1

Electricity can be produced in power stations and from batteries.

*An electric current is a way of transferring energy.

Electricity can be extremely dangerous.

Electricity can be used in different ways to provide lighting and heating, and to make things work.

CIRCUITS

3.2

For an electric current to flow there must be a complete circuit.

Some materials, such as metals, will conduct electricity – these are called conductors. Others, such as rubber, will not conduct electricity – these are insulators.

ALTERING THE FLOW OF ELECTRICITY

3.3

Switches can be used to break circuits, altering or stopping the flow of an electric current.

MAGNETS

3.4

Magnets are mostly made from iron or alloys of iron.

*Magnets can produce pushes and pulls (forces) and so attract iron and steel objects.

Magnets can also attract and repel each other.

(*Asterisks indicate ideas which will be developed more fully in later key stages.)

Sources and uses of electricity

AREAS FOR INVESTIGATION

◆ General ideas about electricity in everyday life.

◆ Looking at the sources of electricity, the use of batteries, and the generation of electricity.

In the *Using energy* teachers' guide there are activities in the 'Energy sources' and 'Mechanisms' themes that may be combined with work on electricity generation.

KEY IDEAS

◆ Electricity can be produced in power stations and from batteries.

◆ Electricity can be extremely dangerous.

◆ Electricity can be used in different ways to provide lighting and heating, and to make things work.

◆ *An electric current is a way of transferring energy.

(*Asterisks indicate ideas which will be developed more fully in later key stages.)

A LOOK AT sources and uses of electricity

For most domestic purposes, the source of our electricity is the mains, a battery or, occasionally, solar power.

Much of the danger associated with electricity is from high voltage sources. The mains supply is a high voltage source – 240 V. Domestic batteries and solar power sources are low voltage sources; for example, most domestic batteries are between about 1.5 V and 12 V. Although the mains supply is safe when used in properly insulated electrical appliances it would be very dangerous to use it in school electricity experiments.

The voltage of a source is a measure of its electrical 'strength'. Thus, in a circuit made up of a battery and a bulb, replacing the battery with another of higher voltage increases the flow of electricity, so that the bulb appears brighter.

The electrical energy for the mains supply comes from power stations; the vast majority of power stations in this country are coal, gas or nuclear fuelled. A supply of electricity can come from solar or wind power, and some watches, calculators, toys and games use solar power to provide their electrical energy.

Finding out children's ideas

■ STARTER ACTIVITIES

1 General ideas

Children will have experienced electricity in their homes, playing with toys, at school, and so on.

To find out some of the general ideas children have about electricity, they could be asked some of the following questions:

What do you know about electricity?
Can you write down three things you know about electricity?
Can you think of some of the ways we use electricity?
Can you draw some of the things in your home which use electricity?
Do these all use the same kind of electricity?
What do you think electricity is like?

2 Sources of electricity

Ask the children to write about, draw, or discuss their ideas about where electricity comes from. Some of the following questions may be useful:

Where do you think electricity comes from?
How does the electricity reach the school or your home?
Do you think that electricity can be made?
How is electricity made?

To see whether the children are aware of both mains electricity and electricity from batteries, ask:

Do you think that batteries are a safe form of electricity?
Why do you think we can safely use batteries?

Children's ideas

1 General ideas

When asked to write three things about electricity, children may suggest some of the following ideas:

> *Electricity is used for homes.*
> *Electricity gives us light.*
> *A heater uses electricity.*
>
> *Electricity can shock us.*
> *Electricity costs a lot of money.*
> *Electricity comes from the Sun.*

Children are usually aware of many of the uses of electricity as well as some of the dangers.

When asked how we use electricity, children were able to think of many uses, mainly connected with the home. The following examples are typical:

> *You will find if you have an electric cooker that it uses electricity. I have electricity in all of my lights.*
>
> *In every house there is electricity.*
>
> *Electricity is very useful. Electricity is part of our lives.*
>
> *Electricity is a very strong form of power, it runs all sorts of things ... it would be hard to live without it.*
>
> *We could not live without electricity.*

These examples show that children regard electricity as essential in their everyday lives, but apparently they tend to associate electricity with the mains rather than batteries.

Children are also aware of the heating effect of electricity.

Electricity is hot ... fire ... comes from big gas things.

Electricity gives us warmth.

If electricity has been left on for a long time, it would be very hot.

It makes your house warm.

Burns you ... when I was a baby, I went to hospital.

When asked about what they thought electricity is like, children said:

Electricity is like magic.

You cannot see electricity.

Electricity is like lightning that comes from space – it hits the wires that are on the street and it goes to the top of your house to make the telephone work.

It must go very fast ... faster than Concorde because you can phone to France in about 10 seconds, so electricity can get to France that quickly!

2 Ideas about sources of electricity

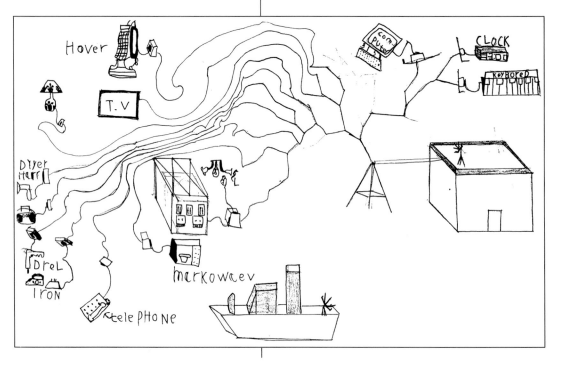

Many city children have the idea that electricity comes from under the ground, whereas children from the country may be more aware of overhead wires strung on poles and pylons as a means of carrying electricity.

When children were asked where electricity comes from, the following responses were typical:

Electricity comes from lightning. It goes underground and then comes up again. When it is another rainy day, it makes more electricity when lightning comes.

From the Sun.

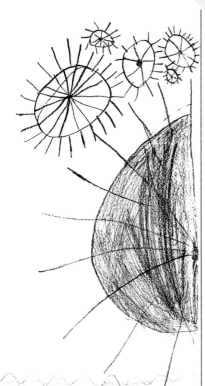

electricity can be made by the force of water because when water flows thru the wheels it can make electicity.

It comes from electricity boards. Boards where they turn the electricity on with switches. It gets there through the wires.

power Station

The power Station Sends off Electricty underground to houses.

The wires reach in to a plug socket and when you turn the tv on you get a picture

... underground – it gets there by tube.
It's made from flint.

powerstation

deciRIcity comes from a powerscenen

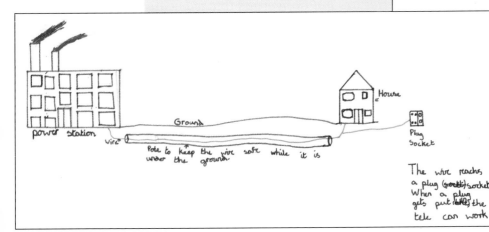

power station

wire

Ground

House

Pole to keep the wire safe while it is under the ground.

Plug Socket

The wire reaches a plug (socket) socket. When a plug gets put into the tele can work.

33

From the ground. Men put electricity in the ground with a big machine – it gives electricity to the ground.

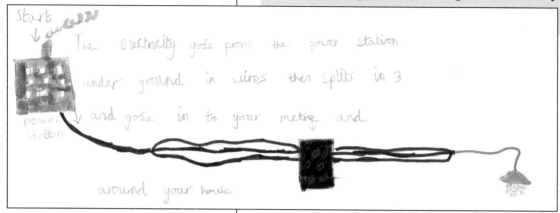

I think it comes from the phone line.

No idea!

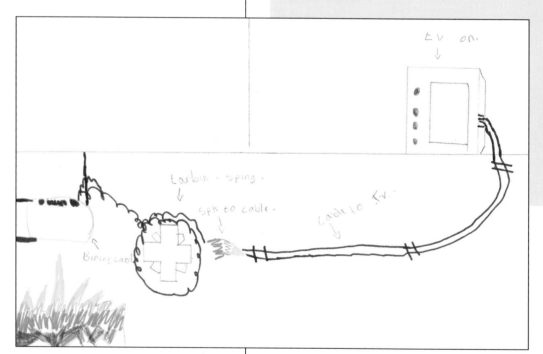

From a mains box somewhere through a wire. It comes from an even bigger electricity box somewhere. It's made by fire – it gets to my house through wires.

When children were asked why they thought batteries are safe to use, the following were typical responses:

Batteries are not dangerous to use because they have a plastic coating – you can't see the electricity!

Batteries are safe because all the electricity is inside them.

If you touch it with your hand, it doesn't electrocute you!

It's dangerous, it's hot, your hands will stick to it.

Helping children to develop their ideas

The chart on the next page shows how you can help children to develop their ideas from starting points which have given rise to different ideas.

The centre rectangle contains a starter question.

The surrounding 'thought bubbles' contain the sorts of ideas expressed by children.

The further ring of rectangles contains questions posed by teachers in response to the ideas expressed by the children. These questions are meant to prompt children to think about their ideas.

The outer ovals indicate ways in which the children might respond to the teacher's questions.

Some of the shapes have been left blank, as a sign that other ideas may be encountered and other ways of helping children to develop their ideas may be tried.

Sources of electricity 1: Batteries

You could ask children to find out where batteries are used in the home and at school.

Children could look through magazines to find electrical

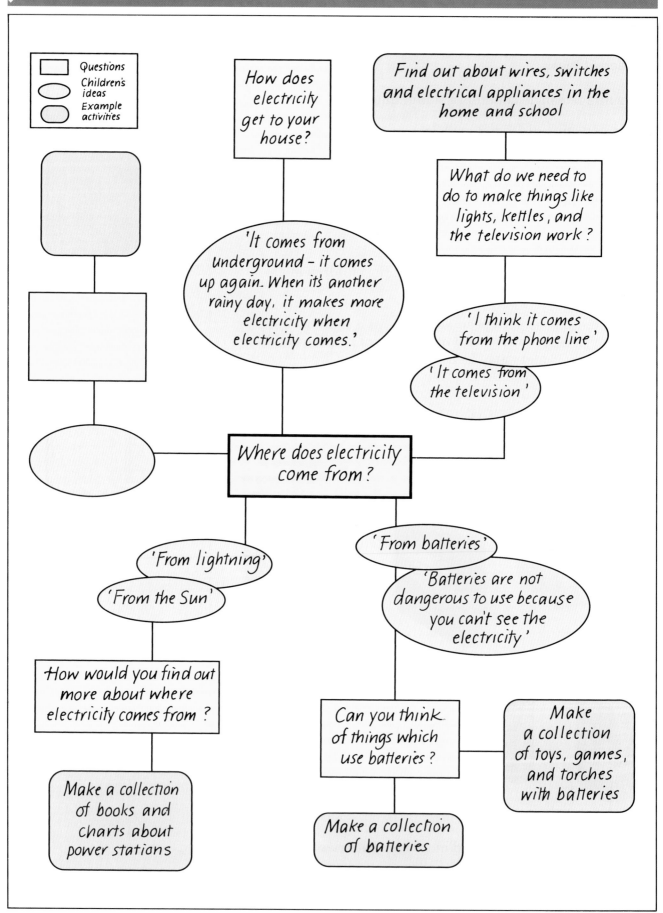

Questions

Children's ideas

Example activities

How does electricity get to your house?

Find out about wires, switches and electrical appliances in the home and school

What do we need to do to make things like lights, kettles, and the television work?

'It comes from underground – it comes up again. When it's another rainy day, it makes more electricity when electricity comes.'

'I think it comes from the phone line'

'It comes from the television'

Where does electricity come from?

'From lightning'

'From the Sun'

'From batteries'

'Batteries are not dangerous to use because you can't see the electricity'

How would you find out more about where electricity comes from?

Can you think of things which use batteries?

Make a collection of toys, games, and torches with batteries

Make a collection of books and charts about power stations

Make a collection of batteries

equipment that is powered by batteries. There are examples of the use of batteries in *Electricity and magnets* and *More about electricity and magnets*.

The children could discuss and show their findings. They could be asked:

Q *Are all batteries the same?*
Do you think that batteries are safe to use?
Why do you think batteries are used for some equipment, not the mains?

Electricity and magnets and *More about electricity and magnets* draw attention to electrical safety.

Provide the children with a selection of batteries, or encourage them to make their own collection. The children could be asked:

Q *Are all the batteries the same?*
What are the main differences between them?

The children will probably notice that the batteries have the voltage marked on them. Ask the children if they know what this tells us, and how they might find out what effect the voltage has on a piece of equipment.

Ask the children to test lightbulbs with more than one battery joined together. (Activities in which children connect bulbs into circuits can be found in 'Simple circuits', pages 47-52.)

Q *Does it make any difference to the brightness of the bulb if there is more than one battery?*

 pb 3.1

 pb

e

t ALL BATTERIES HAVE TWO CONNECTIONS

t THE VOLTAGE OF A BATTERY IS A MEASURE OF ITS ELECTRICAL STRENGTH; A BATTERY WITH A HIGHER VOLTAGE GIVES A HIGHER CURRENT (HIGHER FLOW OF ELECTRICITY) IN A CIRCUIT

t USE 2.5 V OR 3.5 V BULBS; 1.5 V BULBS MAY 'BLOW'

Try connecting batteries of different voltages to an electric motor.

Q *Does using a different battery alter the speed of the motor?*

Sources of electricity 2: Generating electricity

It is possible to use a bicycle dynamo in the classroom to show how electricity can be produced. These dynamos can be easily unscrewed from a bicycle, or bought fairly cheaply.

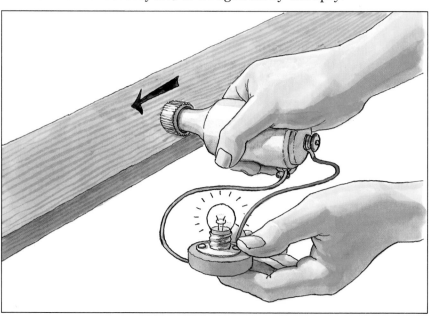

By running the wheel of the dynamo along a flat piece of wood, children will be able to generate enough electrical energy to make a 5 V bulb light.

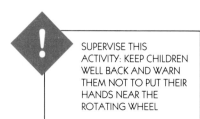
SUPERVISE THIS ACTIVITY: KEEP CHILDREN WELL BACK AND WARN THEM NOT TO PUT THEIR HANDS NEAR THE ROTATING WHEEL

Alternatively you could bring a bicycle with a dynamo into the classroom. If the bicycle is stood upside down and its wheel spun, the lights will work. The children could be asked:

 What provides the energy to produce the electricity?

Electric motors will act as dynamos when they are rotated. Get the children to connect an electric motor to a bulb, and to wrap twine around the spindle of the motor. If the children rotate the motor by pulling hard on the string the bulb will light. Ask the children:

 Where do you think the energy is coming from to light the bulb?
Can you think of any ways in which you could get the bulb to be brighter?

The children may want to devise ways of turning the electric motor. However, the motor needs to be spun rapidly to produce enough power, and if they try to gear up the system the mechanism will produce too much friction.

Some children may be familiar with items in the news about power stations, especially nuclear power stations. They may be interested in finding out about other ways of producing electricity, and can be referred to secondary sources. Many suitable materials are available from the Electricity Association.

The children could show the different types of power station in a wall display. (Further activities on energy sources and power stations can be found in the *Using energy* teachers' guide.)

AT 1   COMMUNICATING

Electricity and magnets and *More about electricity and magnets* provide information about generating electricity, power stations, supplying electricity, and pollution associated with electricity production. Children could find out what electricity is used for in their home or school – *More about electricity and magnets* provides a starting point. They may also find 'Clues to life without electricity' in the latter book useful in discussions.

pb

Circuits

AREAS FOR INVESTIGATION

◆ Making simple electric circuits using lightbulbs.

◆ Making simple electric circuits using motors, bells and buzzers.

◆ Making more complicated circuits.

◆ Conductors of electricity.

KEY IDEAS

◆ For an electric current to flow there must be a complete circuit.

◆ Some materials, such as metals, will conduct electricity – these are called conductors. Others, such as rubber, will not conduct electricity – these are insulators.

A LOOK AT
making simple circuits

Bulbs and batteries have two points of connection. On a battery one of these points may be marked positive and the other negative.

To light a bulb from a battery, wires are connected so that the battery and the bulb form part of a complete circuit. As long as all the connections to the battery and bulb are joined up, and there is no break in a wire or bulb filament, electricity will flow around this circuit until the battery runs out of energy. The flow of electricity in the circuit is from the positive connection of the battery, through the bulb, and back to the negative connection of the battery.

A second bulb can be added to the circuit so that the two bulbs are connected one after the other (series connection), or side by side (parallel connection). Bulbs connected one after the other appear dimmer than bulbs connected side by side.

Any material through which electricity passes is called an electrical conductor. In general metals are good conductors of electricity; copper is a particularly good conductor and is used in electrical wiring. Many non-metals conduct electricity, but, in comparison with metals, they are poor conductors (water and carbon both conduct electricity well). Materials which conduct almost no electricity are called insulators. Common examples are plastics, glass and rubber.

Finding out children's ideas

■ STARTER ACTIVITIES

Throughout this work children should think about the circuit they want to make, and try to predict what they think will happen in the circuit. It is important that the children try out their own ideas, rather than being told what to do.

1 Simple circuits using lightbulbs

Have available bulbs, bulb holders, connecting wires, batteries and crocodile clips.

The children could be asked:

 What do you think you might need to light a bulb?

Allow them to examine the various components available, and give them time to think and discuss what they might use.

Ask them to show their ideas in a drawing.

2 Making simple circuits using other equipment

Once the children feel confident about lighting a bulb, you could offer them other pieces of electrical equipment to try out, for example switches, small electric motors and buzzers.

Before they try out their ideas ask the children to make a drawing, showing how they would connect the equipment.

 Can you draw a picture to show how you would get an electric motor to work?

3 More complicated circuits

This work should be approached with care, as it is possible for children to acquire many misleading ideas about circuits.

The children could be asked:

 Do you think it will be possible to connect two bulbs to one battery?
How could you connect two bulbs to one battery?

Ask them to draw a picture to show how they would do this.

The children could be questioned about their predictions, as follows:

Q *Can you think of another way to connect the two bulbs?*
Do you think the bulbs will be equally bright?
What do you think will happen if you unscrew one of the bulbs?

4 Insulators and conductors

Ask some of the following questions:

Q *What kinds of things do you think electricity will pass through?*
Can you make a list of things which you could try out?

Give the children a collection of materials and ask:

Q *Can you sort these materials into ones which you think will let electricity go through and ones which will not let electricity go through?*

Ask children to show how they would test their ideas.

Q *Can you draw a diagram to show how we could test different things to find out whether electricity will pass through them?*

Allow the children to discuss their ideas with each other.

Children's ideas

1 Ideas about simple circuits with lightbulbs

When asked to predict how they would try to light a bulb, many children think that only one wire is needed.

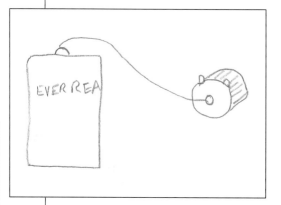

This is understandable, as household appliances appear to be connected to the mains by a single wire. Some children may continue to draw one wire to a piece of electrical equipment even though practical experience shows that two wires are needed.

Some children have an idea of 'positive' and 'negative' associated with electricity, and this may lead them to attach two wires to a battery. Other children may merely be aware of the need for two separate connections.

Although separate connections may be shown at the battery, some children may not be aware that a bulb (or motor, bell etc.) also needs two separate connections.

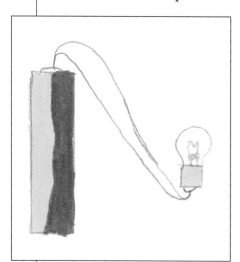

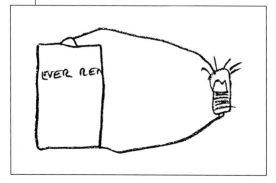

A drawing may show two wires attached to the battery and the bulb, but not to the correct places. This may be a careless drawing, or it may indicate a misunderstanding of where the connections should be made.

Some children will be able to show the connections drawn correctly, especially after practical experience of making circuits using bulbs and other devices.

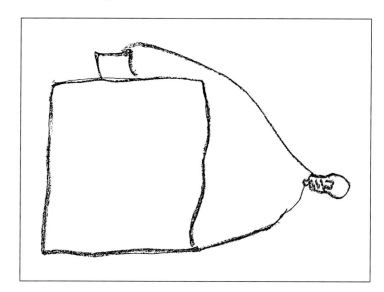

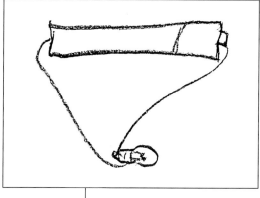

2 Ideas about circuits using other components

Children will not necessarily apply to other devices what they have learnt about making a simple circuit for a lightbulb. For example, this picture shows that the child is unclear about the correct way to connect a motor.

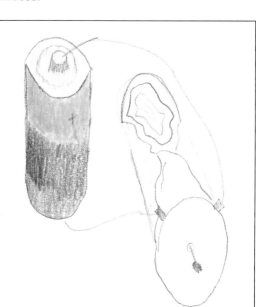

It is possible that the children will need a lot of experience of connecting circuits, using different pieces of equipment, before they can generalize the idea of a complete circuit and the way all equipment should be connected.

3 Ideas about insulators and conductors

Before children have had practical experience of electricity it is likely that some will have little or no idea about materials that conduct electricity. Other children appear to have clear ideas about conductors, as the following two conversations with very young children show.

Teacher	*How do you know which things will let electricity pass?*
First child	*'Cos you see the bulb light up.*
Teacher	*Why does that happen?*
First child	*'Cos it's metal.*

Teacher	*How do you know which things let electricity pass?*
Second child	*They have all got metal.*

It would appear from these conversations that young children can have the concept of a metal, and know that metals conduct electricity.

Older children will be capable of devising their own test to find whether materials are insulators or conductors – for example:

Make a circuit with a break in it, then put the thing you are testing in the break.

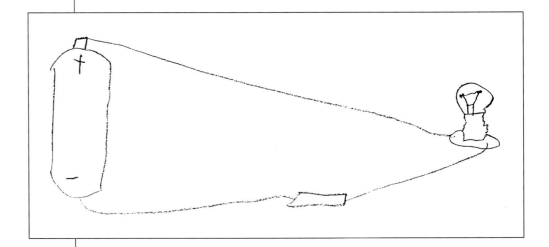

When devising a test for conductors, some children appear to forget earlier ideas about circuits, as this example shows.

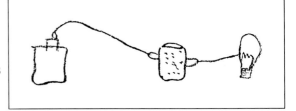

Helping children to develop their ideas

The chart on the next page shows how you can help children to develop their ideas from starting points which have given rise to different ideas.

The centre rectangle contains a starter question.

The surrounding 'thought bubbles' contain the sorts of ideas expressed by children.

The further ring of rectangles contains questions posed by teachers in response to the ideas expressed by the children. These questions are meant to prompt children to think about their ideas.

The outer ovals indicate ways in which the children might respond to the teacher's questions.

Some of the shapes have been left blank, as a sign that other ideas may be encountered and other ways of helping children to develop their ideas may be tried.

1 Simple circuits with lightbulbs

a Lighting a bulb

In the starter activities children were asked to predict and discuss their ideas about lighting a bulb in a simple circuit. Now the children can be given a chance to test their ideas. If they are not successful in getting the bulb to light up, encourage them to discuss why this might be. Ask them to make further suggestions and predictions, and test these.

 ELECTRICITY CAN FLOW ONLY WHEN THE CIRCUIT IS COMPLETE

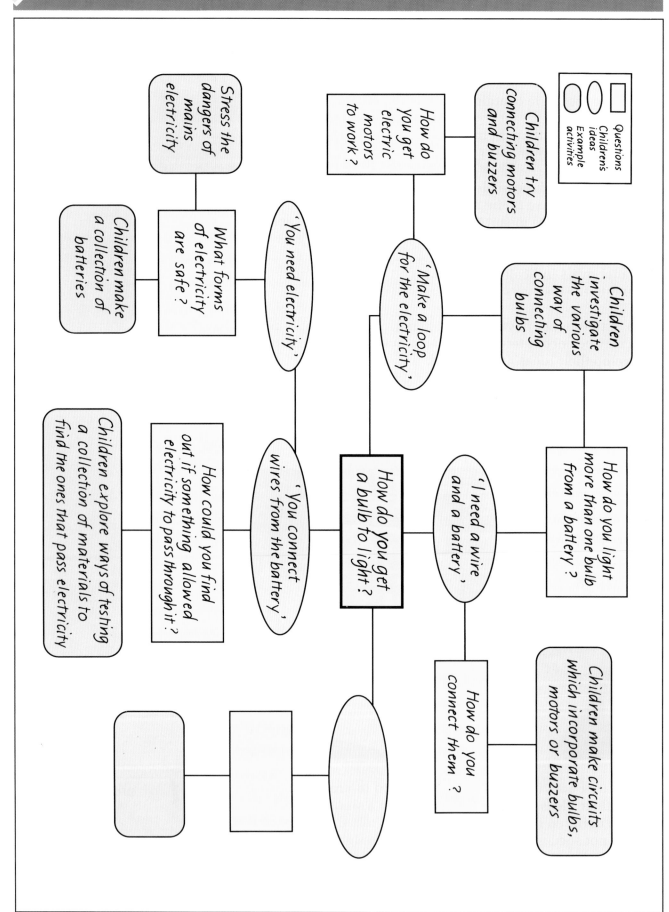

Key:
- Questions (rectangle)
- Childrens ideas (oval)
- Example activities (rounded rectangle)

Children try connecting motors and buzzers

How do you get electric motors to work?

Stress the dangers of mains electricity

What forms of electricity are safe?

'You need electricity'

Children make a collection of batteries

'Make a loop for the electricity'

Children investigate the various way of connecting bulbs

How do you light more than one bulb from a battery?

Children explore ways of testing a collection of materials to find the ones that pass electricity

How could you find out if something allowed electricity to pass through it?

'You connect wires from the battery'

How do you get a bulb to light?

'I need a wire and a battery'

How do you connect them?

Children make circuits which incorporate bulbs, motors or buzzers

When the children are successful, ask them to look carefully at all the connections and to draw a picture showing what they have done.

 AT 1 · COMMUNICATING. OBSERVING

Ask the children to compare their results with others. They could be asked:

Q *Have you connected the bulb in the same way as other children?*
Can you connect the bulb in a different way so that it will still light up?

Get the children to think of reasons why the bulb lit up.

AT 1 · INTERPRETING RESULTS AND FINDINGS

Q *What made the bulb light?*
Where did the electricity come from?
How did the electricity get to the bulb?
What do the wires do?
Where are the wires connected?
What do you think happens to the electricity in the wires?

The scientific answers to some of these questions are not easy, and you may find it helpful to refer to Chapter 5 'Background science'.

Ask the children to annotate their drawing of a circuit to explain why they think the bulb lit up.

Get them to share their ideas with each other. Do all the children give the same explanation for what they think is happening?

b Children's questions

The children may have some very searching questions about what is happening to make the bulb light. It may not be a good idea to try to answer all of these questions, even if it is possible. One suggestion is to allow the children to write down their questions and to display them on the wall. At the end of the work on electricity, they can refer back to these questions, discuss them, and see how many they can now answer themselves.

AT 1 · COMMUNICATING

c Vocabulary work

At various times during the work it may be helpful to introduce the children to some of the following words: current, circuit, energy, conduct, connection, voltage, filament. In *Electricity and magnets* there are examples of how the word 'current' is used in different contexts.

pb

Any new word should be given only when the children need it and when they can understand the context in which it is used.

V

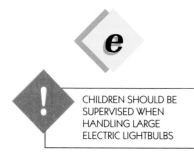

Children are likely to be aware of other circuits, such as running or racing circuits. You could ask them why they think we use the word circuit when talking about electricity.

 In what ways is an electrical circuit like other types of circuits?
Can you write some sentences using the word 'circuit'?

d Looking at lightbulbs more closely

The children may want to know about the part of the bulb that lights up. They could be given a collection of lightbulbs, and asked to examine them under a hand lens.

This collection could include car and mains bulbs, as well as the conventional school science bulbs. It is easier to see the parts in larger bulbs. Ask the children to draw a carefully observed picture showing what is inside the bulbs.

CHILDREN SHOULD BE SUPERVISED WHEN HANDLING LARGE ELECTRIC LIGHTBULBS

After they have examined the bulbs, ask the children if they can think what it is that makes a bulb light up.

 THE ELECTRICITY HEATS THE WIRE (FILAMENT) SO THAT IT GLOWS

 What do you think is special about the wire (filament) in the bulb?
How is the wire in the bulb different from the wire which you used to connect the battery to the bulb?
What happens to the wire when the bulb lights?

e Connecting bulbs to batteries

By using only one type of battery, the children may learn how the wires should be connected to get the bulbs to light, but may fail to understand why a battery should be connected in this particular way. Giving children the opportunity to use a variety of battery types may help them to understand how all batteries should be connected.

Give the children several different types of battery to use in their circuit, and ask them:

 Do you always connect the wires to the batteries in the same way?
Why do we need batteries in a circuit?
How many connecting places do batteries have?
Why do you think batteries have two connections?

Children can find information about batteries in *More about electricity and magnets*.

f Looking at mains plugs

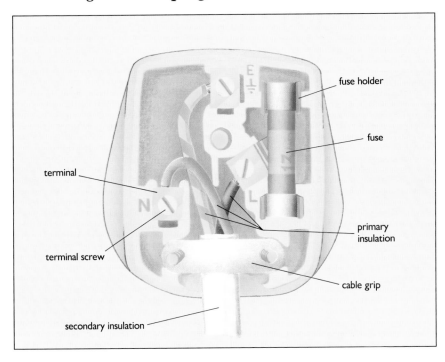

As already mentioned, children may, by observing the single cable used for home electrical equipment, have got the idea that only one wire is needed for a complete circuit. To help them understand that more than one connection is required they can try wiring a three-pin plug to a length of three-strand cable.

Show pupils the correct way to do this:

◆ Remove the minimum of primary insulation.
◆ Make sure that the correct colour wire goes to the correct pin.
◆ Make sure that the secondary insulation (the outer covering) is present right into the plug.
◆ Make sure that the cable grip is holding the cable firmly.
◆ Screw the cover on tightly.

 BATTERIES HAVE TWO POINTS OF CONNECTION, ONE POSITIVE, THE OTHER NEGATIVE

 STRESS THAT CHILDREN MUST NOT INVESTIGATE MAINS ELECTRICITY

 IF THE PLUG HAS BARE WIRES AT THE END IT MUST NOT BE PUT INTO A SOCKET – CHILDREN COULD ELECTROCUTE THEMSELVES

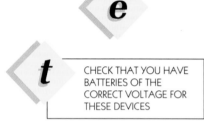

CHECK THAT YOU HAVE
BATTERIES OF THE
CORRECT VOLTAGE FOR
THESE DEVICES

To be safe, the plug should be disabled so that there is no chance of children putting a plug with trailing wires into a line socket. This can be done by bending one of the pins in a vice or attaching a lump of solder to one of the pins. Explain how and why the plug has been disabled.

This may be a good moment to tell children more about how to deal with electrical equipment safely. There is information about electrical safety and the use of mains electricity in *Electricity and magnets* and *More about electricity and magnets*.

2 Using other components in a circuit

To widen their experience of connecting components in a circuit, the children can use buzzers, bells and motors. They could try putting switches in all their circuits.

When the children are connecting motors, ask them to observe what happens when the connecting wires from the battery are reversed.

When the children record their work, ask them to draw all connections carefully. They should try to explain their drawings and give a clear account of how a component is connected to the battery.

It may become too time-consuming for the children to draw batteries, bulbs and so on in detail each time. When you feel that the children are experienced in drawing connections accurately, you could ask them to devise their own shorthand symbols for recording their circuits. Traditional scientific symbols need not be introduced at Key Stage 2.

Once the children are confident that they can connect these components into a circuit, they may find it more interesting to put them into their own models. For example, they could make electrical quiz boards which use buzzers, lights, or bells, robots with eyes that light up or a dolls' house with working lights.

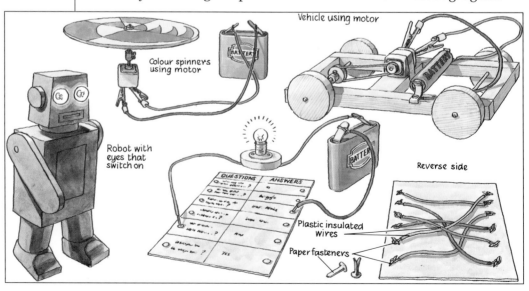

Colour spinners using motor

Vehicle using motor

Robot with eyes that switch on

QUESTIONS   ANSWERS

Reverse side

Plastic insulated wires

Paper fasteners

Ask the children to devise a game for a blind (or sighted) child in which the completion of a circuit operates a buzzer. For example, one group of children covered the inside of a box with plastic foam. Small holes had been cut into the foam, and beneath each of the holes were two pieces of aluminium foil with a gap between them. Some of these pieces of foil were connected to a battery and a buzzer. When a ball bearing rolled into a hole with one of these connections it would complete the circuit and the buzzer sounded. The child then had to answer a question.

The children could invent other games based on the idea of completing a circuit.

3 More complicated circuits

Give the children plenty of opportunity to test their ideas about connecting two bulbs to one battery.

Encourage the children to try different ways of connecting the bulbs. Ask them to think whether the bulbs are really wired differently, or if they have just placed the equipment in a different way on the table. Allow the children to discuss their ideas with each other and to compare their results.

The children could be asked:

Q *What happens if you unscrew one of the bulbs?*
Can you connect a circuit in which unscrewing one bulb puts the other bulb out?
Can you connect a circuit in which unscrewing one bulb leaves the other bulb alight?

Ask the children to think about why other bulbs may or may not be affected when a bulb is unscrewed.

Parallel and series circuits are discussed further in Chapter 5 'Background science'.

 CHECK THAT THE BULBS ARE OF EQUAL RATING – SAME VOLTAGE AND SAME CURRENT

 IN A CIRCUIT IN WHICH BULBS ARE CONNECTED ONE AFTER THE OTHER (SERIES), UNSCREWING A BULB BREAKS THE COMPLETE CIRCUIT. WHEN BULBS ARE CONNECTED SIDE BY SIDE (PARALLEL), UNSCREWING A BULB DOES NOT BREAK THE COMPLETE CIRCUIT IN WHICH OTHER BULBS ARE CONNECTED

AT 1 INTERPRETING RESULTS AND FINDINGS

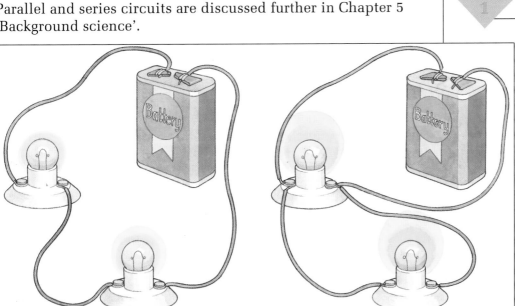

There is no need to explain the terms 'parallel' and 'series' to the children. These terms are more appropriate for Key Stage 3.

Get the children to find out about the brightness of bulbs which are connected side by side, and one after the other.

 Are bulbs equally bright when you connect them in different ways?

The children could discuss their ideas about why the brightness of bulbs changes when they are connected in different ways. However, an explanation would be expected at Key Stage 3 only. (You can find an explanation in Chapter 5 'Background science'.)

4 Insulators and conductors

a Testing materials

In the starter activities children may have tested some materials to see whether these are conductors. They should now be given the opportunity to extend their experience. Again, get the children to devise their own way of testing a range of materials.

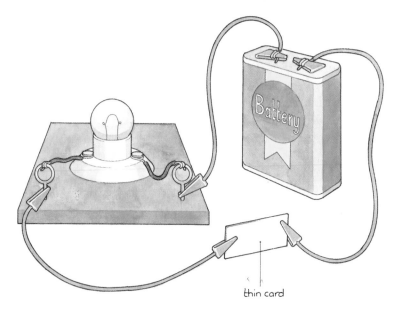

thin card

 BULBS CONNECTED ONE AFTER THE OTHER APPEAR DIMMER THAN WHEN THEY ARE CONNECTED SIDE BY SIDE

 METALS ARE GOOD CONDUCTORS OF ELECTRICITY; SOME OTHER MATERIALS CONDUCT ELECTRICITY, BUT NOT SO WELL

AT 1 PLANNING AND CARRYING OUT FAIR TESTS. INTERPRETING RESULTS AND FINDINGS

If the children suggest only a limited range of materials, for instance only metals, they should be encouraged to try carbon (such as pencil 'lead'), liquids, fabrics, card, glass and plastics.

Encourage the children to discuss their results with others. Where groups disagree, the children could be asked:

 Why do you think the results are different?
Are your circuits the same?
How could you check each other's results?
What other things might happen in your circuit to stop electricity flowing?

The children could record and display their results in a chart.

When it appears that the children are confident about the idea that some materials allow electricity to pass and others do not, it may be appropriate to introduce the words 'conductor' and 'insulator'.

Children can think about how electric currents flow in the human body. *Electricity and magnets* and *More about electricity and magnets* provide information.

b Classifying materials

Separating materials into conductors and insulators could be a starting point for other ways of classifying materials. The children could be given samples of copper, iron, aluminium, wood, paper, and plastic and asked to think of a question that would divide the materials into two groups. Some other tests that the children might think of are as follows:

◆ Is it attracted to a magnet?
◆ Does it float?
◆ Will it bend?
◆ Will light pass through it?

The children could use these ideas to make a branching tree, on paper or perhaps by using a computer program.

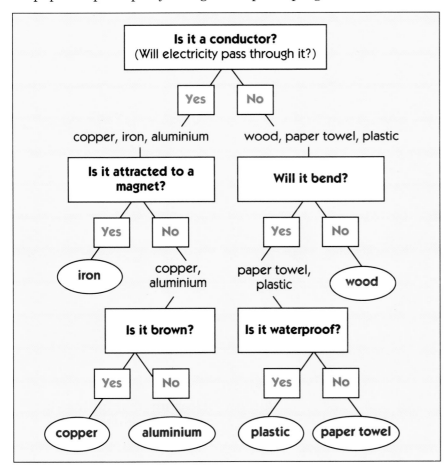

Alternatively, the children could start a database of materials and their properties. (See also the *Materials* teachers' guide.)

Altering the flow of electricity

AREAS FOR INVESTIGATION

◆ Completing and breaking a circuit, using switches, control technology, and AND, OR and NOT gates.

KEY IDEAS

◆ Switches can be used to break circuits, altering or stopping the flow of an electric current.

A LOOK AT
altering the flow of electricity

Switching systems provide a convenient method of breaking or completing a circuit. Some switches are operated manually, others electronically. Dimmer switches regulate the amount of electricity flowing in a circuit.

Logic gates such as AND, OR and NOT gates switch a device on and off in response to the flow of electricity in the gate's input circuits, thus:

◆ NOT gate: a device is switched on when there is NOT a flow of electricity in the input circuit;

◆ AND gate: a device is switched on when there is a flow of electricity in one input circuit AND a second input circuit;

◆ OR gate: a device is switched on when there is a flow of electricity in one input circuit OR in a second input circuit.

Finding out children's ideas
■ STARTER ACTIVITIES

Completing and breaking the circuit: switches

Once the children feel confident that they can complete a simple circuit using a lightbulb, ask them to think of some convenient ways of switching the light off and on. Of course, throughout the work on circuits, the children need to disconnect the equipment so that the batteries do not run down too quickly.

 Can you think how you can make the light turn off? Can you find as many ways as possible of turning the light off? You should be able to find more than six if you look very carefully.

When the children have done this, they can share this information with the other children. They could be asked:

 How did you turn the light off? How many different ways of turning the light off did you find? Why do you think the light goes off when you undo one of the connections?

Get the children to work in pairs. One child should look away while the other undoes (or loosens) part of the circuit. The first child has to check the circuit to find where it is not connected.

Once the children are familiar with the ideas, give them the opportunity to explore a variety of switches, such as a push button switch, lever switch, sliding switch, and plug switch. They could be asked:

 What does a switch do? How does a switch work? Can you think how you could make a switch? How could you turn a switch on? What would make a switch turn off?

Give the children a wide selection of materials, and ask them to invent their own switch.

 Where would you put the switch in a circuit? Do you think it will make any difference where you put the switch in the circuit?

Children's ideas

Because the mechanism of switches is normally concealed, children are not usually very clear about how a switch works. When asked to explain how a switch works, the following responses were typical:

> *By pressing.*
> *By electricity.*
> *When you turn on the switch, you let the electricity through.*

After some experience of using or making switches, children may have clearer ideas about how these work, as these examples show:

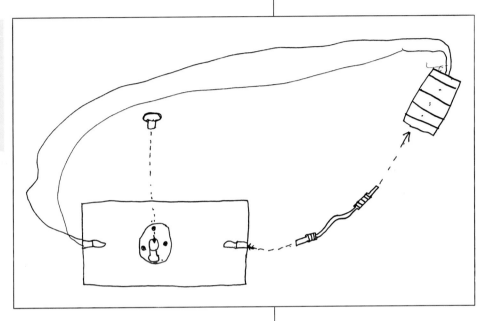

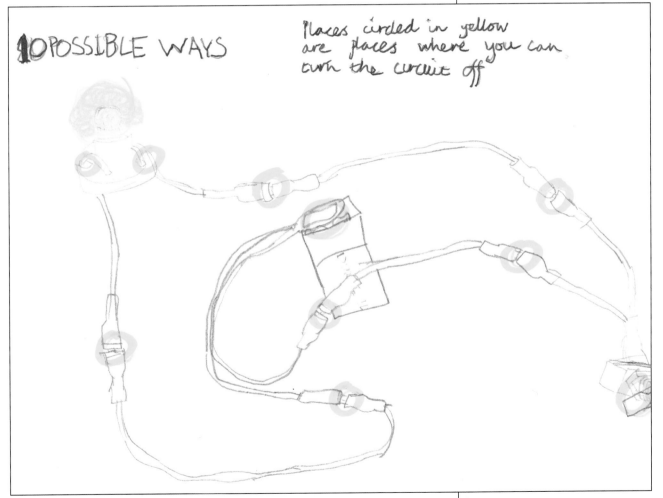

1 POSSIBLE WAYS

Places circled in yellow are places where you can turn the circuit off

The flick switch

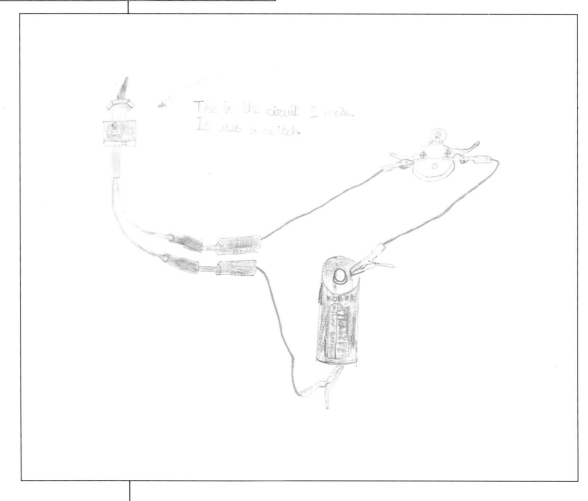

OFF

on

So that when you flick the switch it move the metal plate

When it is on, it allows electricity to pass through but when it is off, it breaks the circuit.
When you push the switch, two wires connect to each other and one of the wires goes to the bulb and the other to the cable.

This is the circuit I made.
It also a switch.

Helping children to develop their ideas

The chart on the next page shows how you can help children to develop their ideas from starting points which have given rise to different ideas.

The centre rectangle contains a starter question.

The surrounding 'thought bubbles' contain the sorts of ideas expressed by children.

The further ring of rectangles contains questions posed by teachers in response to the ideas expressed by the children. These questions are meant to prompt children to think about their ideas.

The outer ovals indicate ways in which the children might respond to the teacher's questions.

Some of the shapes have been left blank, as a sign that other ideas may be encountered and other ways of helping children to develop their ideas may be tried.

1 Making switches

As in the starter activity, ask the children to design their own switches.

 How could you make a switch which will turn a light (buzzer, bell, motor) off?

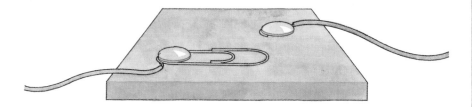

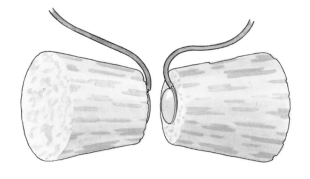

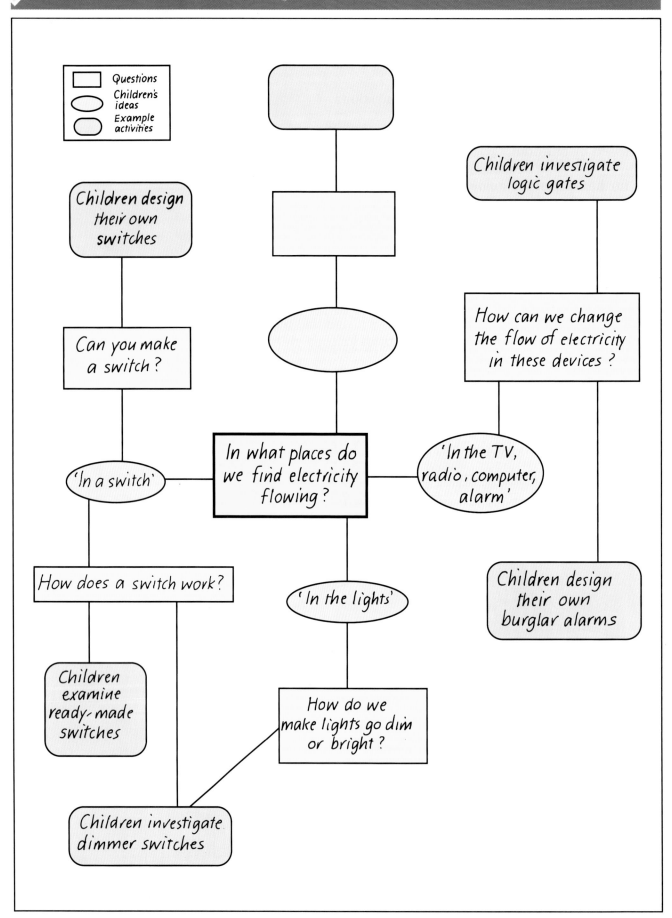

Questions

Children's ideas

Example activities

Children investigate logic gates

Children design their own switches

Can you make a switch?

How can we change the flow of electricity in these devices?

'In a switch'

In what places do we find electricity flowing?

'In the TV, radio, computer, alarm'

How does a switch work?

'In the lights'

Children design their own burglar alarms

Children examine ready-made switches

How do we make lights go dim or bright?

Children investigate dimmer switches

When the children have devised their own switches, they could try them at different places in the circuit. Do they always work?

Q *Do you think it will make any difference where you put the switch in the circuit?*
How many wires will you need when you put the switch into the circuit?

2 Ready-made switches

Give the children a variety of ready-made switches, including a bellpush. Ask the children to try these in different parts of a circuit.

Q *Do they always work?*
Can you explain how a switch works?

AT 1   OBSERVING

If possible, allow the children to unscrew some switches so they can see how they work.

The children could make annotated drawings showing how they think the switch works.

3 Sending messages

The children could be asked:

Q *Can you think how you could use a light and switch to send a message to a friend?*
Which of the switches which you have tried so far do you think would be the best for doing that?
Can you invent a code you could use when you are sending your message?

(The children may wish to refer to a secondary source to find out about the Morse code.)

Children could think about how sounds are produced by electricity. *Electricity and magnets* would provide a starting point.

4 A switch game

In this game the metal ring acts as a switch. When the two pieces of metal connect, they complete the circuit. Once shown how to make one the children can devise their own variations.

During this activity there may be a good opportunity to find whether children understand the idea of a complete circuit.

Q *How do you think this game works?*
What makes the bulb light?

5 Making dimmer switches

Many children will have come across dimmer switches in domestic lighting or as slide switches on electrical equipment. Here are two fairly easy ways for children to make dimmer switches for themselves.

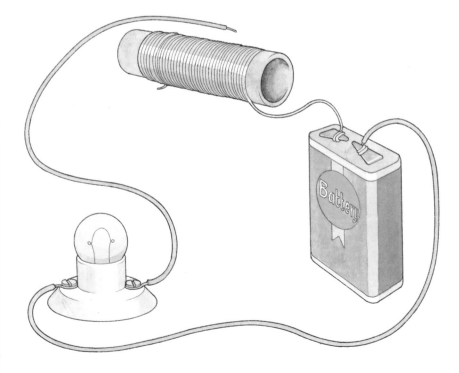

Make a coil by winding nickel chrome wire around a cardboard tube, and connect the coil as shown in the picture. Hold the end of one wire in contact with the coil, and be move it along it to see what effect this has on the light.

Another way of making a dimmer switch is to split a pencil open, and touch one of the wires at different points along the pencil lead. Ask the children to observe what happens to the lightbulb as you slide the wire along the lead.

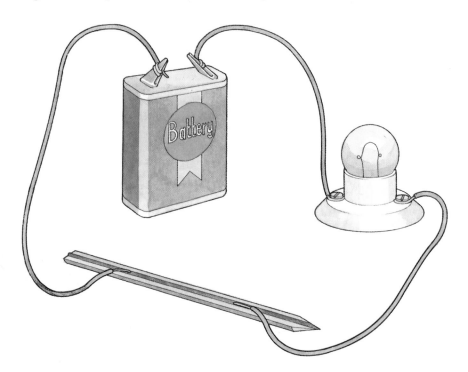

Q *How do you think a dimmer switch works?*

The children could annotate drawings of one of the switches to show their explanation of how it works.

Note that a modern mains dimmer switch is electronic and does not work in this way. A radio volume control – both the revolving type and the straight slider type – does use carbon and it may be possible to dismantle an old one to show the children.

6 Making burglar alarm systems

Children will have fun inventing their own burglar alarm systems. To help them with their designs, you might show them a pressure switch and a pendulum and ring switch, and switches worked by magnetic catches. Ask the children:

Q *How do you think these switches work?*
Can you think of how these switches would be useful?

t THE NICKEL CHROME WIRE REDUCES THE FLOW OF ELECTRICITY IN THE CIRCUIT

t THE PENCIL 'LEAD' IS MADE OF CARBON, WHICH REDUCES THE FLOW OF ELECTRICITY IN THE CIRCUIT

AT 1 INTERPRETING RESULTS AND FINDINGS

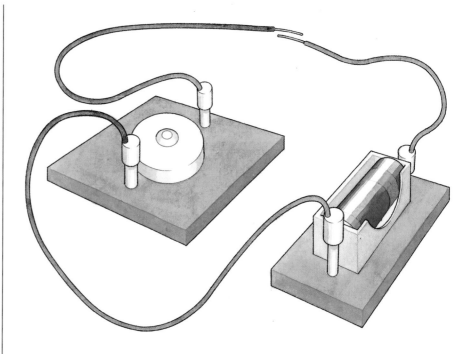

The pressure switch works when two pieces of wire are pressed together to make a connection. Ready-made pressure switches are available, or children could try to invent their own.

SIMPLE BURGLAR ALARMS ARE SET OFF BY BREAKING AN ELECTRIC CIRCUIT

In the pendulum and ring switch one contact is loosely suspended, and the other contact is in the form of a ring surrounding the first. When the switch is moved the contacts touch. These switches are used in car burglar alarms.

Magnetic catches are also used on windows and doors to trigger alarms. The two halves of the catch form the contacts, and are held firmly together by magnetism when the door is shut. Children may want to design their own magnetic catches for alarm systems, or they could fix wires to ready-made catches of the kind sold for kitchen cupboard doors.

The children could be presented with a problem on designing electrical circuits and alarm systems, as follows:

'You decide to hide a treasure box in a dark cave. When you visit the cave, you will need to be able to turn the light on, to check that your treasure is still there.

'You will also need to invent a burglar alarm system to warn you of anyone entering the cave to steal your treasure.

'You will need to be able to switch the burglar alarm off when you enter the cave.'

7 Using a computer as a switching mechanism

A computer is essentially a sophisticated form of switching mechanism. One of the simplest ways to demonstrate this is to use control technology to operate bulbs, motors or buzzers.

For this you will need a control box connected to the computer, and the appropriate software. This equipment is relatively inexpensive and will provide endless possibilities for children to devise their own simple programs.

Using the computer, a range of equipment can be switched on and off through a sequence. For example, children will be able to:

◆ make lights flash in sequence;
◆ get a buggy to drive forwards and back;
◆ make a robot with flashing eyes.

Children could make their own models or use construction kits for this work.

The children will have to write a suitable program for the computer they use. A Basic program to run two flashing lights would need to go through something like the following steps:

```
Switch on 1; switch off 2.
Delay loop of 2 seconds.
Switch off 1; switch on 2.
Delay loop of 2 seconds.
Go to start.
```

Other uses of a simple program of this kind are to switch a motor on and off, and to operate a pulley system so that it will wind up and down.

Once children are familiar with this use of a computer they will think of many ways to use it. For instance, one lower junior class made a model fairground with flashing lights and working rides.

Another class made a Nativity scene. Mary and Joseph travelled to the stable by a belt-driven system, the star flashed in the sky, the angels ascended and descended (operated by pulleys) and the stable door opened!

8 AND, OR and NOT gates

AND, OR and NOT gates are common in domestic electrical equipment.

An example of an AND gate

A washing machine will work only when the door is closed AND it is switched on.

Children could incorporate an AND gate into their burglar alarm systems. The burglar alarm would work only if someone stepped on the pressure pad (which acts as a switch) AND the alarm was switched on.

An example of a NOT gate

Street lights come on when it is NOT light.

Children could put a light sensor into a circuit to illustrate this. Covering up the sensor would switch on a bulb connected into a circuit. In other words, the bulb will give out light when light is NOT reaching the sensor. For this reason the sensor has to be shaded from the light.

An example of an OR gate

An alarm clock radio will play when you switch it on OR when it is switched on by the alarm.

Children could try putting two switches in parallel in a circuit. The light will work when one switch OR the other is turned on.

There are electronic kits available which help children to understand AND, OR and NOT gates.

e

Magnets

AREAS FOR INVESTIGATION

◆ Investigating the properties of magnetic and non-magnetic materials.

◆ Investigating the forces between magnets.

◆ Using magnets to find direction.

◆ Exploring the magnetic effect of electricity.

KEY IDEAS

◆ Magnets are mostly made from iron or alloys of iron.

◆ Magnets can also attract and repel each other.

◆ *Magnets can produce pushes and pulls (forces) and so attract iron and steel objects.

(*Asterisks indicate ideas which will be developed more fully in later key stages.)

A LOOK AT magnets

Magnets attract objects made of iron or steel. When a magnet is brought near such objects they become magnetic themselves, and are attracted. Removing the magnet causes the object to lose most of this magnetism. Steel tends to retain magnetism more than pure iron.

A magnet is demagnetized to some extent by hitting or dropping it.

The Earth is itself magnetic: it attracts a freely suspended magnet, causing it to settle in a north–south direction. The end of the magnet pointing towards the Earth's North Pole is called the north pole of the magnet. The south pole of the magnet points towards the Earth's South Pole. When magnets are brought together with their north poles facing, or their south poles facing, there is a force of repulsion between the magnets; north and south poles of magnets attract each other.

A flow of current through a wire produces magnetism (a magnetic field) around the wire itself. This effect continues as long as the current flows. If an iron nail is put into the coil, the magnetism is even stronger. This combination of coil and nail is an example of an electromagnet.

Finding out children's ideas

■ STARTER ACTIVITIES

You might ask some of the following questions:

 What is a magnet?
*Can you draw (and write about) what you think
a magnet is?*
*If I gave you a collection of different objects, can you
think how you could find out which ones are magnets?*
What are magnets made of?
Do all magnets look the same?
*Can you think of some of the differences between
magnets?*
Draw some of the magnets which you have seen.
How do you think a magnet works?

Children's ideas

Children may think that magnets have some sort of magical
properties, or they may try to associate the way a magnet works
with more familiar items which also have 'sticking' properties;
for example:

> *It has some sort of glue on it …*
>
> *It has all these little things inside it which make it
> stick.*

Children are likely to recognize as magnets only those kinds
they are familiar with, for example horseshoe magnets.

Helping children to develop their ideas

The chart on the next page shows how you can help children to develop their ideas from starting points which have given rise to different ideas.

The centre rectangle contains a starter question.

The surrounding 'thought bubbles' contain the sorts of ideas expressed by children.

The further ring of rectangles contains questions posed by teachers in response to the ideas expressed by the children. These questions are meant to prompt children to think about their ideas.

The outer ovals indicate ways in which the children might respond to the teacher's questions.

Some of the shapes have been left blank, as a sign that other ideas may be encountered and other ways of helping children to develop their ideas may be tried.

Words and ideas

Once the children have understood the concepts involved during the following activities, it may be appropriate to introduce some of these words: attract, repel, pole, magnetic. The children should try to use these words in their own sentences.

In all these activities it is more important for the children to understand the ideas than to learn scientific terms.

1 Magnetic materials

What does a magnet attract?

Provide the children with different magnets and a collection of objects, which should include various metals and non-metals.

Ask the children to predict what might happen when the objects are tested with a magnet.

 What kind of objects will a magnet pick up (attract)?

After investigating the collection, the children could test other materials in the classroom.

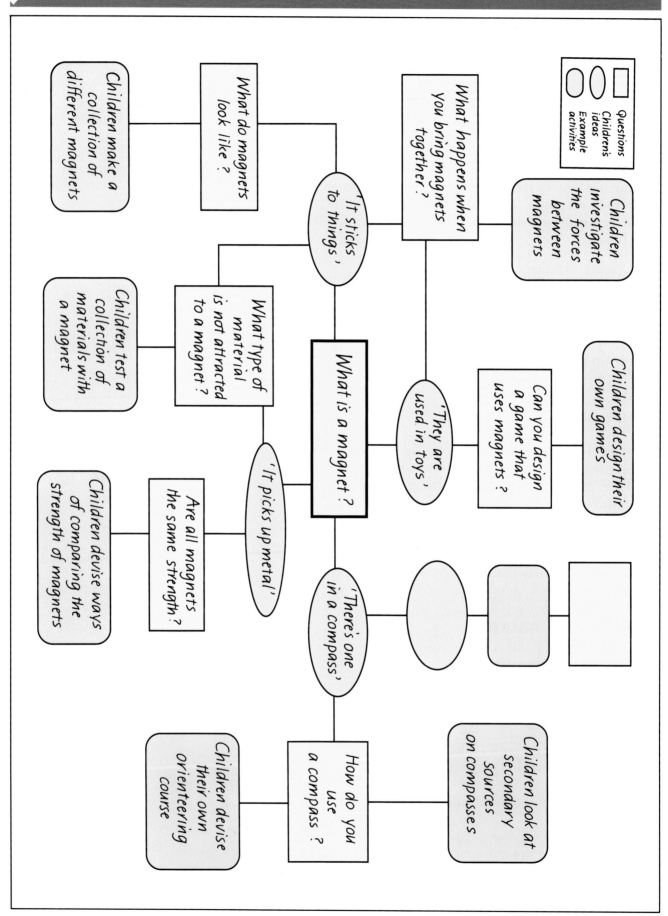

Key:
- Questions
- Children's ideas
- Example activities

What is a magnet?

'It sticks to things'
- What do magnets look like? → Children make a collection of different magnets
- What happens when you bring magnets together? → Children investigate the forces between magnets

'It picks up metal'
- What type of material is not attracted to a magnet? → Children test a collection of materials with a magnet
- Are all magnets the same strength? → Children devise ways of comparing the strength of magnets

'They are used in toys'
- Can you design a game that uses magnets? → Children design their own games

'There's one in a compass'
- How do you use a compass? → Children devise their own orienteering course
- Children look at secondary sources on compasses

Get the children to discuss and display their findings. They could be asked:

 What do you think is attracted to magnets?
Are these things all made of the same materials?

Ask the children to think of some practical ways in which they could use magnets.

 How can you use magnets to pick things up?
Why do you think people often keep magnets in their sewing kits?

The children could use a magnet to investigate a drink can. The tops of many drink cans are made of aluminium and the sides out of steel. Most food cans are made out of steel. The children could go on to find out how cans are sorted for recycling by using powerful magnets.

Ask the children to invent their own 'recycling plant' for detecting iron or steel goods.

 Can you think how you could make your own recycling plant which will separate iron and steel from other materials?

The children could think of using magnets to help in classifying materials (see page 72).

Children can read about the discovery of magnetism and uses of magnets in *Electricity and magnets* and *More about electricity and magnets*.

2 Forces and magnets

a Testing the strength of magnets

The children could be given a selection of magnets and asked:

 Are all magnets the same strength?

Get the children to devise a fair test to find which is the strongest magnet.

Are they going to test just one end of each magnet?

If they use paperclips, will they drag the magnet through the paperclips, or will they put it in the middle of the pile? The children could be asked:

 How can make sure you carried out a fair test?

INTERPRETING RESULTS AND FINDINGS

pb

e

PLANNING AND CARRYING OUT FAIR TESTS

The children should think about how to record their results. A bar chart or a computer database would be appropriate.

Children could find out whether magnets can attract things through different materials. They could be asked to predict what would happen with: paper, wood, card, water, a table, a book.

After the children have tested their ideas they could be asked:

Q *Can you use this idea to invent some games using magnets?*

For example, the children could make a paper 'car' and attach a paperclip to it. The car could be 'driven' along a road drawn on a card by using a magnet.

b Exploring the push and pull of magnets

Ask the children to predict what they think will happen if they put two magnets together.

Q *What will happen if you turn one of the magnets round?*

Give the children the opportunity to experiment with different magnets so that they can observe what happens when two ends of a magnet are brought together. Many, but not all, toy magnets have a painted mark on the north pole. You might mark all the magnets in this way.

 OPPOSITE POLES OF A MAGNET (NORTH AND SOUTH) WILL ATTRACT EACH OTHER AND STICK TOGETHER; LIKE POLES OF A MAGNET WILL REPEL ONE ANOTHER

Ask the children to discover for themselves which poles are attracted to each other and which are repelled.

It is fun for children to feel the effect of magnets pushing each other away. For this they need two strong magnets.

AT 1 INTERPRETING RESULTS AND FINDINGS

Another interesting effect can be produced by putting disc magnets with holes in the centre on a dowel rod. The children can then actually observe the 'pushing power' of the magnets.

Ask the children to invent a game which uses the idea that magnetic poles will either attract or repel each other. For example, they could try to connect a sentence in the right order by covering bar magnets with words which connect together in only one way; or they could make a model train which could be coupled together only if the carriages were facing in a certain direction.

3 Using magnets to find direction

Give the children a compass to look at. Ask them:

  What is a compass ?
What use is a compass?
What do you notice about the compass needle?

Ask the children to point with both arms, showing the direction of the needle. They can look at others, compare and discuss their results. Ask:

What have you found out about the direction of the needle?
Why does the needle point like this?
Could you use a compass to help you in any way?

To find how a magnet can be used as a compass, the children can suspend a magnet in a paper sling and wait for it to settle. An alternative method is to float a magnet on a flat piece of wood and watch the way it points.

Ask the children to think of how this idea was adapted to help people find their way around. They can read about it in *Electricity and magnets* and *More about Time and Space.*

OBSERVING.
INTERPRETING RESULTS
AND FINDINGS

COMPASS NEEDLES ARE
SMALL MAGNETS;
BECAUSE THE EARTH
ACTS LIKE A GIANT
MAGNET, IT ATTRACTS
THE NEEDLE OF THE
COMPASS SO THAT IT
ALWAYS POINTS
NORTH–SOUTH; THE
POLE WHICH POINTS
NORTH IS CALLED THE
'NORTH POLE'

Once the children are familiar with the way a compass works, they could invent their own orienteering course in the school grounds. If possible, use proper orienteering compasses, as they are more accurate. An example of an orienteering route is as follows:

1 Walk on a bearing of north-east until you reach the double doors.

2 Go through the doors and turn east for about 10 metres until you reach a large plane tree.

3 From the tree, walk south-west until you reach a path.

4 Walk north along the path to the hall.

5 From the entrance to the hall, find the bearing which would take you back to your classroom.

The children could devise routes for others to follow, perhaps using the treasure map in *Electricity and magnets*.

4 Using electricity to make a magnet

One of the effects of a flow of electricity is to produce magnetism. Children can use this to make a magnet, and an electromagnet. The children need a large iron nail, 2 metres of thin insulated wire, a large battery, a switch and some crocodile clips.

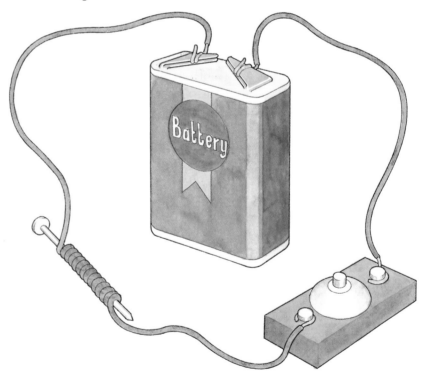

Get the children to wind about 50 turns of wire around the nail, and then to connect a switch and a battery so that a current can be passed through the coil. Note that this improvised magnet uses a lot of current and will exhaust even a large battery in a couple of minutes, so it should be used only for short periods.

You might ask:

 How could you test the nail to see if it is a magnet? What will happen to the nail when the electricity is switched off? Will it still act like a magnet?

The children could try out their ideas and find what happens when the current is switched on and off. They could be asked:

 How strong is the magnet? Is it as strong as some of the other magnets which you tested?

The children could show how they think the nail is magnetized by writing and drawing.

They could use secondary sources to find out about the uses of electromagnets in industry, starting with the one in *More about electricity and magnets*.

 3.4

t ELECTRICITY FLOWING IN A WIRE PRODUCES MAGNETISM AROUND THE WIRE; IRON OR STEEL NEEDS A SOURCE OF ENERGY TO TURN IT INTO A MAGNET; IN THE CASE OF AN ELECTROMAGNET, THIS ENERGY IS PROVIDED ELECTRICALLY

 pb

CHAPTER 4

Assessment

4.1 Introduction

You will have been assessing your children's ideas and skills by using the activities in this teachers' guide. This on-going, formative assessment is essentially part of teaching since what you find is immediately used in suggesting the next steps to help the children's progress. But this information can also be brought together and summarized for purposes of recording and reporting progress. This summary of performance has to be in terms of National Curriculum level descriptions at the end of the key stages, and some schools keep records in terms of levels at other times.

This chapter helps you summarize the information you have from children's work in terms of level descriptions. Examples of work relating to the theme of this guide are discussed and features which indicate activity at a certain level are pointed out to show what to look for in your pupils' work as evidence of achievement at one level or another. It is necessary, however, to look across the full range of work, and not judge from any single event or piece of work.

There are two sets of examples provided. The first is the assessment of skills in the context of the activities related to the concepts covered in this guide. The second deals with the development of these concepts.

4.2 Assessment of skills (AT1)

Things to look for when pupils are investigating electricity and magnetism, as indicating progress from level 2 to level 5:

Level 2: Making suggestions as well as responding to others' suggestions about how to find things out about a simple circuit or compare materials in terms of magnetic properties. Using equipment, such as batteries, wires, bulbs and bulb holders and magnets, to make observations. Recording what they find and comparing it with what they expected.

Level 3: Saying what they expect to happen when something is changed and suggesting ways of collecting information to test their predictions. Carrying out fair tests, knowing why they are fair, and making measurements. Recording what they find in a variety of ways; noticing any patterns in it.

Level 4: Making predictions which guide the planning of fair tests. Using suitable equipment and making adequate and relevant observations. Using tables and charts to record measurements and other observations. Interpreting, drawing conclusions and attempting to relate findings to scientific knowledge.

Level 5: Planning controlled investigations of predictions which are based on scientific knowledge. Using equipment carefully, repeating observations as necessary. Using line graphs to record and help interpretation; considering findings in relation to scientific knowledge.

James, Ricky and Stuart, in a Year 4 class, undertook a simple investigation of the effect of a magnet. They were asked by their teacher: what are magnets?

Ricky: *Things stick to them.*

The other children agreed.

The teacher showed them a group of objects and asked if they could predict which ones would stick to a magnet. The children discussed the objects with each other, and appeared to decide that metal objects, or objects that had metal parts, would be attracted to a magnet. The children drew their predictions and tested the objects. Ricky and James indicated on their drawings which of their predictions were correct.

James

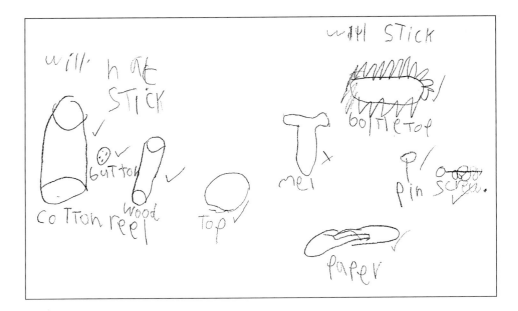

Ricky

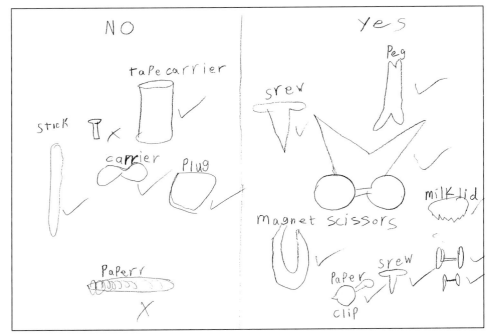

Stuart

WILL not stick.

TOP

buTTon

wood

cOTTon reeL

The matal box did not stick.

WiLL stick

MeTaL box

boTTLe Top

pin

screw

PapercLip

The teacher asked each child what they had found out. They replied as follows:

Stuart: *Magnets stick to metals and some other magnets.*

Ricky: *Magnets stick to metal things.*

James: *Magnets stick to magnets, but sometimes the magnets don't stick to the metal. They stick to proper metals like paper clips.*

The children made predictions about what they expected to happen to each object, then compared what they found out with their expectations. In drawing conclusions, Stuart says that magnets stick to metals even though he tested a metal to which the magnet did not stick. Only James concluded that there was a difference between metals in terms of magnetic properties, but his reference to 'proper metals' suggests that he may still think that the ones that stick to the magnet are the only 'proper' ones. These features indicate that the work is at level 2. All three children would benefit from discussing their observations more fully at the end of their investigations.

Investigations were carried out on simple circuits by year 5 children who had previously done some work on electricity in Year 4. This work gives an opportunity to assess the children's understanding as well as their investigation skills.

The teacher asked Sheena, Arly and Rajam to light a small bulb. They could choose any equipment they needed. After lighting the bulb, they described what they thought was happening to the circuit. When they finished the teacher asked each of them to see if they could light a bulb.

The teacher asked Sheena to find other ways of lighting the bulb and to describe what she thought was happening in the circuit when the bulb lit up.

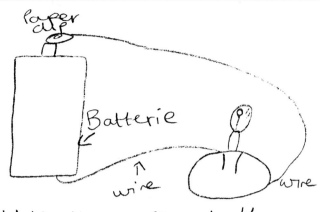

Batterie

wire

wire

Well the wire at the bottom travels electricity to the bulb and some how the wire leading to the top attached we a paper clip will make the bulbs light up.

Arly

Sheena

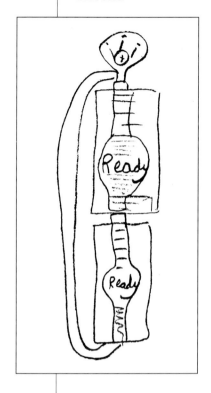

A ~~circuit~~ the battery has points of positive energy and negetive energy. When both tipes of energy are some how passed onto the buld the bulb lights up.

Rajam

Sheena

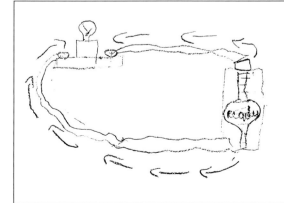

The electricity flows from the battery to the light bulb

Ready

GooD	BAD
Nail	Plactic
Scraw	peeier wood
paper clip	lego
metal wire	Straw
Pin	crad
metal chree	(Paper)
cliper	
Hook	
scissors	
Butterfly clip	
piol	

Most of the things that wroked were metal pieces. The things that did not wrok were wood platic and (parper) card.

Arly was given various objects and a variety of materials and asked to devise a way of finding out whether electricity passed through any of them. After completing her second circuit, Sheena was also given this task.

Sheena and Arly showed how they would test the materials. Then they carried out their own test.

Rajam was asked to light two bulbs from one battery and find different ways of switching them on and off.

After Rajam completed this work, the teacher asked him to light two bulbs with one battery, and to arrange it so that each bulb could be switched on and off separately from the other bulb.

Sheena

Arly

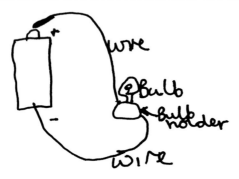

wire
Bulb
Bulb holder
wire

Do the diagram shown here then on the Top wire put something the a paper clip and the if the bulb lights up that mean electricity can go though the object

It is only Metel that works

Spring   yes
paper clip   yes
crocadile clip yes
curly must   yes
cottom wool   no

To get two bulbs to light from one battery.
=

This is how I think it will work

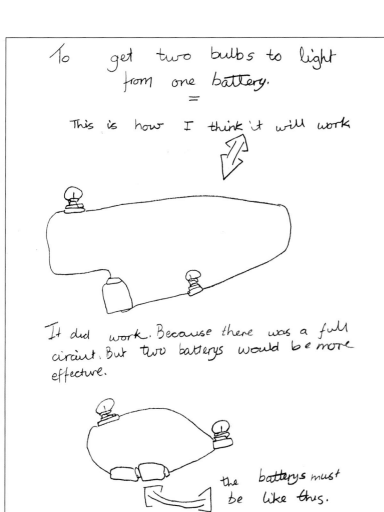

It did work. Because there was a full circiut. But two batterys would be more effectue.

the batterys must be like this.

Rajam

Rajam

One On and one swith
=

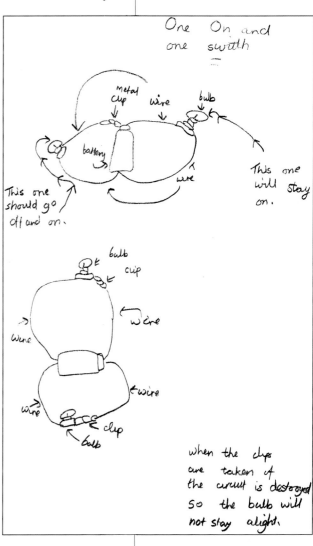

metal clip   wire   bulb

battery

wire

This one should go off and on.

This one will stay on.

bulb

clip

wire

wire

wire

clip

bulb

when the clips are taken of the circuit is destroyed so the bulb will not stay alight.

Rajam

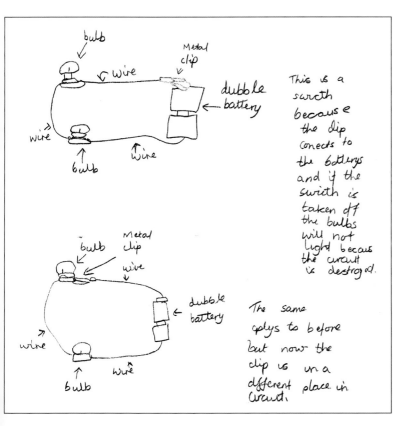

bulb

wire

Metal clip

dubble battery

wire

wire

bulb

This is a swicth because the clip conects to the batterys and if the swicth is taken of the bulbs will not light becaus the circuit is destroyd.

bulb   Metal clip

wire

dubble battery

wire

bulb   wire

The same aplys to before but now the clip is un a different place in circut.

Sheena and Arly used their knowledge of electric circuits to devise a way of testing materials to see if they would conduct electricity. Arly makes explicit the basis of the test, that if the bulb lights when an object is in the circuit then electricity must pass through it. They tested all the objects in the same way. Their results are consistent with the objects tested and they drew a general conclusion. This investigation gives no opportunity for close observation or measurement, however other aspects of their investigation suggest work at level 3.

Rajam also plans his circuit before using it and in this respect makes predictions about what will work. He communicates his prediction and findings clearly, making good use of drawings. Having carried out the test of his circuits he explained aspects which made them work. The limitations of this type of investigation prevent any assessment of Rajam's investigation skills in general, but in respect of using predictions in planning, communicating through annotated diagrams and explaining findings in scientific terms, his work is at level 4.

4.3 Assessment of children's understanding (Part of AT4)

Aspects of work relating to electricity and magnetism indicating level 2 to level 5:

Level 2: Constructing a simple electrical circuit to make a bulb light. Sorting materials according to whether or not they are magnetic.

Level 3: Knowing that an unbroken circuit is needed to make a bulb light and using this knowledge to suggest why a bulb in a particular circuit may not light up. Knowing that there is attraction and repulsion between magnets and attraction between magnets and magnetic materials.

Level 4: Using different types of switches in a circuit and explaining how they control the electricity. Constructing circuits in which there is more than one device and circuits in which each device is controlled by a separate switch.

Level 5: Knowing how to connect different devices, such as bells, variable resistors and relays into their circuits and have some idea of their electrical effects. Using diagrams to represent series circuits and following such diagrams in constructing circuits.

The work of Stuart, Ricky and James indicates ability to sort materials, which is an aspect of level 2. They would need more opportunities to explore magnets to help their progress towards level 3.

From Sheena's drawing showing electricity flowing from the battery to the bulb (page 83) it appears that she does not use the accepted model of an electric current to explain the flow of electricity in the circuit. The same seems to be true of Arly. Nevertheless their explanations, together with the circuits they constructed, show that they know how to connect a bulb into a complete circuit and that a complete circuit is necessary for electricity to flow, fitting this aspect of the description of work at level 3.

Their teacher could help their progress by giving them more experience of work at this level and providing them with opportunities to connect other devices, such as a buzzer and an electric motor into circuits, and to devise their own ways of switching a current on and off.

Although Rajam's mental model of electricity is in terms of positive and negative electricity (which is inaccurate and unhelpful), he appears to understand the idea of a complete circuit and that breaking a circuit acts as a switch. He has been able to devise and connect simple circuits in which bulbs can be switched on and off together, or separately, indicating work at level 4. He is also able to represent series and parallel circuits in diagrams, thus showing progress towards level 5. To extend his experience Rajam would benefit from opportunities to use different types of devices in circuits and to begin to understand their effects.

CHAPTER 5

Background science

What is electricity?

Adults and children alike often have confused ideas about electricity. The word is used in everyday life to describe the mains electricity supply. But what does it really mean?

Everything is made of atoms. An atom has a central nucleus orbited by a cloud of smaller particles called electrons. The central nucleus contains positive electric charges whilst the electrons are negatively charged. Most electrons stay in orbit, but the outermost ones can sometimes be detached, or extra ones added. An atom which has fewer or more than its normal number of electrons is said to have an **electric charge**. A lack of electrons results in a **positive** charge; a surplus produces a **negative** one. A charged atom is called an ion.

How electric charge behaves

Left – *Uncharged balloon and sweater*

Right – *Negatively charged balloon, positively charged sweater*

Electric charge can be moved from place to place, and from one object to another. When you rub a balloon on your sweater, you knock electrons off the wool on to the rubber, as the electrons are less firmly attached in the substances of which wool is made. The balloon takes on a negative charge, and the sweater a positive one. Such a charge remains in place for some time, so it is known as **static charge**. Eventually the extra electrons in the balloon will slowly move across to the wool and the two charges cancel each other out. This takes several hours in

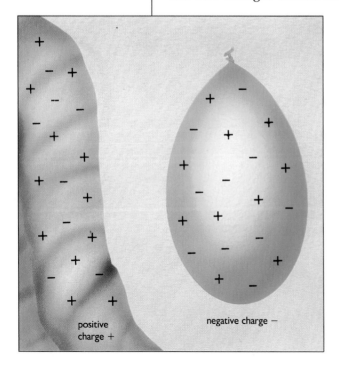

positive charge +

negative charge −

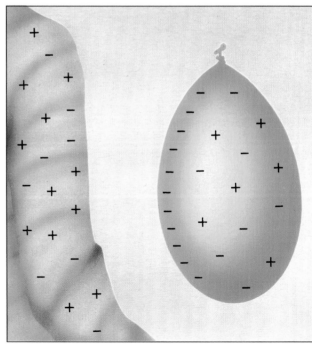

substances in which electrons do not move easily, such as rubber. A positively charged object attracts a negatively charged one, so that the balloon sticks to the sweater. A charged object also attracts uncharged objects, and will pick up small scraps of paper. However, two objects with the same electric charge repel each other. This **electrostatic attraction** and **repulsion** may sound rather like magnetism (see below); but they work differently.

Electric current

When a charge moves, the flow is called an **electric current**. (This flow is explained below.) The movement can transfer energy. When a current goes through the filament of a lightbulb, the moving electrons flowing along the narrow wire shake its atoms, so that the wire heats up. The more current flows, the hotter the filament gets and the brighter it glows. In school science, a bulb is often used as a rough measure of the size of a current. Electricians, engineers and scientists use a more accurate device called an **ammeter**. Current is measured in **amps** (A for short).

Circuits

When an electric current flows through a device, it cannot be sent along one wire. The current does its work not by filling the device with electrons, but by moving them through it. The current must therefore flow in a **circuit** – a circular route from the source of energy, through the device and back to the source. So two wires run between the source and the device.

This is not apparent when you look at, say, a table lamp, because its wires are inside a single casing. That can cause both children and adults to see electric current as a 'fuel' being fed down the wire, as if down a pipe, to the lamp, and 'used up' in it.

Bicycle model of direct current transmission

A simple model of what actually happens is a bicycle wheel driven by a chain. The chain is the circuit, and each link represents an electron. When you put energy into the pedals the chain transfers energy to the wheel, which turns. The chain goes round endlessly. The links are not 'used up'. It is not their substance, but their movement, which carries the energy.

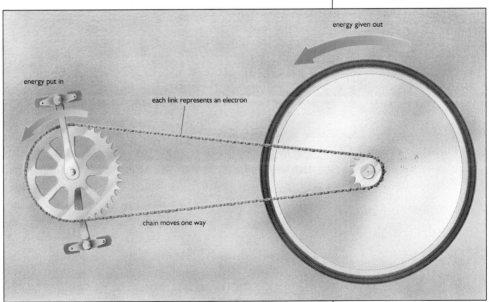

energy given out

energy put in

each link represents an electron

chain moves one way

The chain always moves in one direction. You can turn it the other way (ignoring the fact that a real bicycle has a freewheel mechanism). But to get any useful work done by the wheel you have to keep turning the pedals in the same direction. This models the transfer of energy electrically from a battery, in which a current flows in a constant direction. It is called **direct current** (DC for short).

A direct current circuit is shown below. The battery supplies energy to move electrons, corresponding to the energy your feet put into the bicycle pedals. The electrons, corresponding to chain links, go round the circuit. As they pass through the bulb they do work, lighting the bulb. That corresponds to the work the wheel does in moving the bicycle. The electrons are not used up, and their number remains constant.

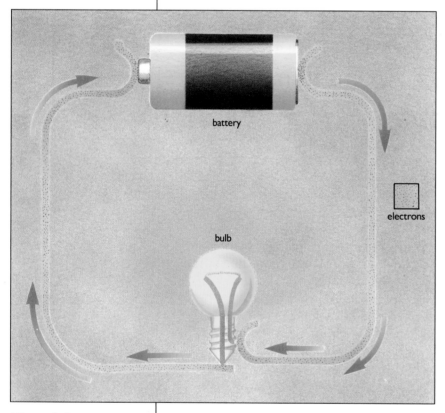

battery

electrons

bulb

Flow of electrons in a circuit

The diagram shows the direction that the electrons actually flow – from the negative terminal (the flat end of the battery) around the circuit to the positive terminal (the end with the cap). (Some textbooks conventionally show the current flowing from positive to negative.)

The energy produced by the battery comes from chemicals. When these are used up, the battery goes flat. It is not the electrons which are used up. They are still there, but there is no energy to push them.

Electrical resistance, conductors and insulators

When you turn a bicycle chain, not all the energy you put in does useful work. Some ends up heating the metal and air because of friction. Similarly, in a circuit some energy produces unwanted heating effects. It takes energy to push electrons through materials. All materials offer some resistance to the flow of current. This is called **electrical resistance**. Metals have only a slight resistance, which is why they are used to make the wires in circuits. Copper has very little resistance, so it is used to make wires. A material with a low resistance is called a **conductor**. Another conductor is graphite (the 'lead' in pencils). This has a slightly higher resistance than metals.

Some materials offer a very high resistance, allowing almost no electric current to flow through. These are called **non-conductors** or **insulators**. They include plastics, glass and rubber. Electric wiring is covered with plastic to make sure that electric charge stays in the wire, and does not travel through other pieces of metal or humans that may touch the wire.

Certain materials have a moderate amount of resistance. They are called **semi-conductors**. These are of no use in simple devices such as torches and electric motors; but they are employed in electronic devices, where current has to be controlled in complex ways.

A thin wire has more resistance than a thick one, because it has fewer electrons to carry the energy. It is the electrical resistance of a wire which produces the unwanted heating effects mentioned earlier.

Mains electric current, voltage and wattage

Mains electric current differs from that provided by a battery in two ways.

It is more powerful – there is more energy to push electrons. The pushing force of a source of electrical energy is called **voltage**, and is measured in **volts** (symbol V). The mains supply in Britain is at 240 V. A simple torch battery gives 1.5 V. Voltage is not the same as the amount of current. Compare a piped water supply. Voltage represents the pressure of the water, and current the quantity of water that flows in a given time.

The amount of energy a current transfers depends on both the voltage and size of current (number of amps). It is measured in **watts** (symbol W). Electrical appliances are often marked with their wattage – the amount of energy transferred a second. A 60 W bulb uses more power, and gives more light, than a 40 W one.

Mains current is not direct: it is **alternating current** (AC for short), which flows first one way, then the other. The direction reverses itself very quickly. In Britain the mains supply runs at 50 cycles a second (50 **hertz** or Hz), which means that it goes one way then the other 50 times a second.

It does not matter which way current flows to light a bulb. You do not notice the bulb flickering, because the current changes direction so quickly. Some devices have to be specially designed to work on one type of current, for example motors. A DC motor will turn backwards if you reverse the battery in the circuit. An AC motor always turns the same way.

To understand how alternating current can do work, think of a chain drive again – but this time turning a grindstone. If you turn the crank backwards and forwards, the chain links will move backwards and forwards, and the grindstone will move back and forth too. Whichever way it turns, it will still grind. You might object that if you reverse the

Grindstone model of alternating current transmission

direction of the handle 100 times a second, the stone will not move far enough to do useful work. But electric current travels so fast – hundreds of thousands of kilometres a second – that there is no problem.

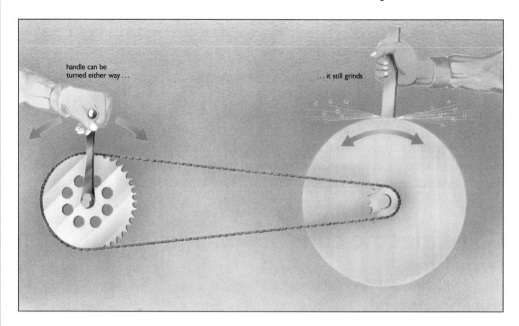

handle can be turned either way...

... it still grinds

The mains supply uses AC for two reasons. First, it can be produced by simpler machines than those used to generate DC. Second, only AC will work a **transformer**. This is a device for changing the voltage of an electricity supply. When electrical energy is sent through cables across country, some power is 'lost' warming the cables because of their resistance. At 240 V no useful energy would be left after a few kilometres. In fact it is sent at a much higher voltage, as much as 400 000 V, and losses are much slighter. This would be a dangerous voltage to have in your home, so the voltage is changed with local transformers before it is sent the final short distance to your home.

Mains electricity is produced in power stations by **generators** driven by consuming fuel of some kind, such as coal, gas, nuclear fuel – or sometimes by water power. When you pay for 'electricity' what you are actually paying for is the fuel used, and for building and maintaining the equipment. The amount you use is measured in **kilowatt hours** (kWh) – a consumption rate of 1 kilowatt (kW, equal to 1000 W) for 1 hour, or of 500 watts for 2 hours. A one bar electric fire rated 1 kW will consume 1 kilowatt in 1 hour – a kilowatt-hour.

Electric shock

An **electric shock** occurs when a large amount of electrical energy flows through your body. This can burn you, destroy your nerves, or even kill you.

The severity of an electric shock depends on the size of the electric current that flows through you. Most serious shocks come from the mains supply, which has a high voltage and can deliver plenty of electrical energy. If you were to touch a 400 000 V power line you would get an even worse shock which would certainly be fatal. A torch battery could not harm you, as the voltage is too low to push a sizeable current through you. You can also get a sharp but harmless shock from a static charge. Static charges have voltages of up to 1 million volts, but the current is tiny. Often a static shock is accompanied by quite a big **electric spark**. The distance a spark can travel through dry air is about 1 cm for every 20 000 V.

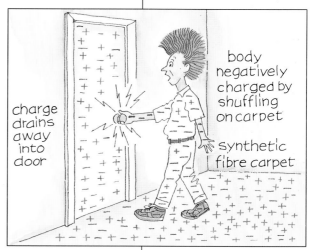

Static electric shock

You are more likely to get a static shock on a dry day. Electric charge trickles away much more easily into moist air, so you cannot build up much charge. A good way to get a static shock is to shuffle your feet on a synthetic carpet, which builds up a charge on your body. Synthetic fibres are good insulators, so that the charge cannot trickle away into the floor. Then touch a door handle, and all the charge will rapidly drain through your arm into the door, giving you a shock. You often get static discharges when putting on a synthetic fibre pullover. The crackling noise is due to tiny electric sparks. If your hair stands on end as well, it is because each hair has the same charge, so they repel each other.

A mains shock happens when electric current goes through your body into the ground. The supply travels to your home along two wires, the '**live**' wire and the '**neutral**' wire. For technical reasons the neutral wire is connected to the ground at the transformer. So if you touch the live wire, you will complete a circuit via the live wire, your body, the ground, and the neutral connection at the transformer.

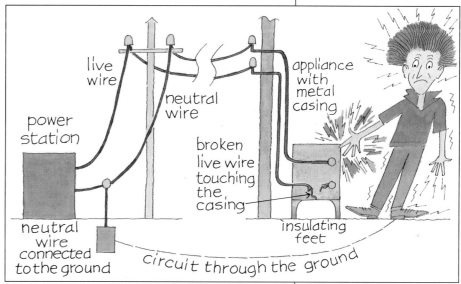

Mains electric shock

Although your skin does not conduct electricity well, enough current goes through your body to do serious harm. It is much worse if you have wet hands, which makes your skin more conductive. The contact between your feet and the ground does not conduct well either, but resistance is lowered if the floor is wet. That is why there are strict laws about switches and electric plugs in bathrooms. The ground itself offers almost no resistance, not because it is made of good conductive materials but because it is so enormous.

A common cause of electric shock is that the 'live' wire inside an appliance with a metal casing has come loose and is touching the casing. Danger can be avoided here by **earthing** the casing. The cable supplying the appliance contains a third wire. This is connected to the casing at one end and, via the plug, socket and house wiring, to the ground at the other end. If the live wire comes loose and touches the casing, there will now be hardly any resistance between the live wire and the ground. A massive current will flow. Inside the plug, the live wire is connected to its plug pin through a **fuse**. This is a little cartridge which contains a thin wire. A current of normal size, as when the appliance is switched on, will go through this wire without incident. But a very heavy current will heat the wire so much that it melts, thus 'blowing' the fuse and cutting off the supply to the appliance. House wiring also has more fuses in a fusebox on the wall, to provide extra protection. However, a weakness of fuses is that they take several seconds to 'blow', by which time you could be dead. ELCB (Earth Leakage Circuit Breakers) detect tiny currents to Earth and instantaneously break the live connection.

Earthing an appliance

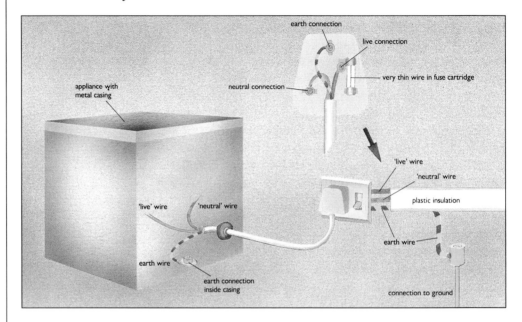

Model dimmer

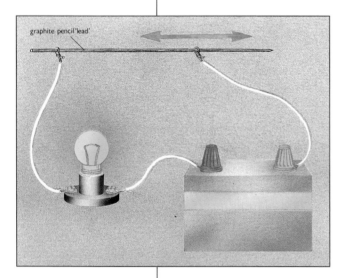

Volume control

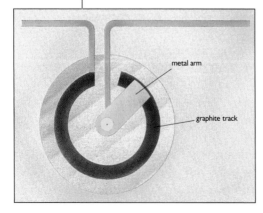

Varying resistance

The electrical resistance of an object is measured in **ohms** (Ω, the Greek letter omega, for short). If the resistance is doubled and the voltage remains constant, the flow of current will be halved. If the resistance is halved, twice as much current will flow.

It can be useful to vary the resistance in a circuit, since this allows you to control the amount of current that flows. A convenient material to use is graphite, as it conducts electricity moderately well. You can use a graphite pencil 'lead' to vary the brightness of a small bulb. By sliding the wires together along the 'lead', you can reduce the distance the current has to go through the graphite, and so brighten the bulb. This principle is used in the volume control of a radio, which has a metal arm sliding along a track of graphite. However, the dimmers used for room lighting are electronic devices which work in a completely different way.

Switches

A **switch** is a gap in a circuit which can be opened and closed. When the gap is open the circuit is broken, and no current flows. The working parts of a switch are **contacts** – pieces of metal which can move together or apart. The complicated construction of a mains switch is simply to ensure that the contacts move together and apart quickly and firmly. This reduces electric sparking, which would otherwise soon burn away the metal.

A switch will work no matter where it is in a circuit. However, in mains appliances the switch is always in the live wire. This is for safety. An appliance with its live wire interrupted cannot cause a shock.

Avoiding short circuits

If you had a torch with a metal casing, and the bulb was connected to the battery with bare wires which touched the casing, the current would not get to the bulb. It would take the route of least resistance through the casing – a **short circuit**. Short circuits are always unwanted and often dangerous. In a torch, the low resistance of the casing would allow so much current to flow that the battery would go flat in seconds. With the mains or a car battery, a short circuit can overheat wires or cause sparking. With luck, the high current will blow a fuse before any damage is done. Cars also have fuses.

Series and parallel connection

Bulbs in parallel

A circuit can supply current to two or more devices, for example lightbulbs. These can be connected into the circuit in two ways. If they are side by side, this is known as connection in **parallel**. Both bulbs shine as brightly as they would if each was connected to a separate battery. The battery lasts only half as long as it would with one bulb. The filament of a bulb has considerable resistance because it is thin. Since the bulbs are side by side, the effective width of the wire is doubled, the resistance in that part of the circuit is halved, and twice as much current flows. All the appliances in a house are connected in parallel. When you turn on an extra light, you supply more energy electrically.

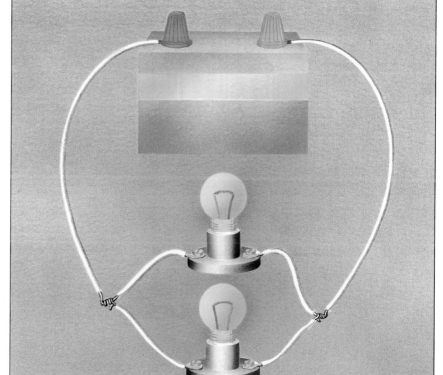

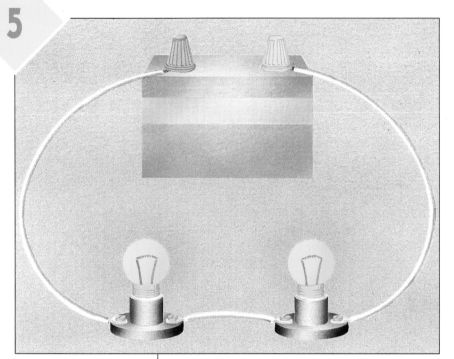

Bulbs in series

If the bulbs are in a line they are said to be in **series**. This has the opposite effect on the resistance: it is doubled. Only half as much current flows, and the bulbs glow dimly. But the battery lasts twice as long. A familiar example of series connection is Christmas tree lighting. A set has 20 bulbs similar to those used for car dashboard lights. If a single bulb were connected to the mains, its filament would melt. But because there are many bulbs in series, the current is reduced to a level which is just enough to light them all.

If one bulb in a series fails, all the lights go out. If one bulb connected in parallel fails, the others stay lit.

Ways of generating electricity

Batteries produce electric current by a chemical reaction. When one chemical substance reacts with another, electrons move from the atoms of one substance to the atoms of the other. Reactions between certain chemicals can create a flow of electrons which have sufficient energy to travel round a circuit and do useful work. When all the substances in the battery have reacted, the battery is flat. Some batteries can be recharged by sending a current through them in the opposite direction, reversing the reaction and reconstituting the original chemicals.

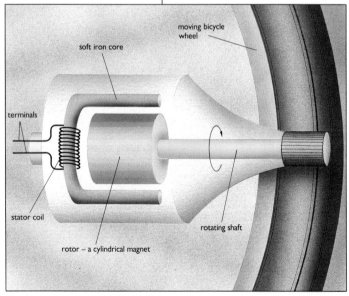

Diagram of bicycle dynamo

Generators rely on the fact that when a wire and a magnet move past each other, the magnetism causes a current to flow in the wire (see the next section). Energy in the form of movement is put into the machine, which transforms this energy into electric current. An example of the simplest form of generator is a bicycle 'dynamo'. A magnet spins next to a coil of wire wound on an iron core, which strengthens the effect. In any generator, the moving part is called a **rotor** and the stationary part a **stator**. In the type shown, the rotor makes current flow one way for half a turn, then the other way during the other half turn. The machine therefore produces AC.

Strictly speaking, a dynamo is a DC generator. The device shown is really an **alternator**. DC generators need switching devices to keep the current flowing in the same direction.

If electric current is fed into a generator, it creates magnetism and causes the wire coil and the magnet to move relative to each other – in fact, the machine works as an **electric motor**. Essentially a generator and a motor are the same machine. If you attach a motor to a light bulb, wrap cotton thread around the pulley and pull it rapidly, the bulb will light.

Magnets

A **permanent** magnet is a piece of metal which has been magnetized. Only a few metals can be strongly magnetized, and only some of these stay magnetized for any time. Most permanent magnets are of iron, often combined with nickel and cobalt.

Magnetism is caused by the behaviour of electrons – not travelling electrons, but those which remain in orbit in their atoms. They spin in a certain direction, causing a magnetic force. If most of the atoms in a piece of iron are aligned so that the spins are in the same direction, the iron is magnetized as shown here. This can be done by stroking the iron in one direction with a piece which is already magnetized. The magnetic force of the magnet aligns the atoms in the other piece of metal in the same direction. This is called **magnetization by induction**.

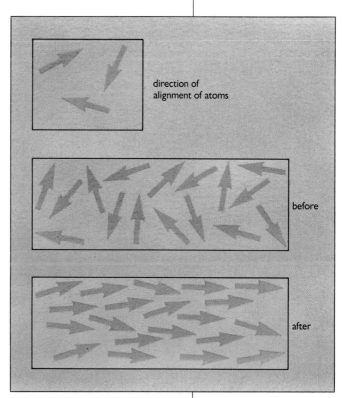

A piece of iron before and after it has been magnetized

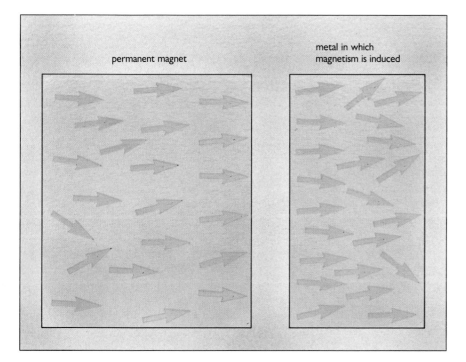

Magnetic induction

A magnet has two ends, which are called the north and south poles. The north pole of one magnet attracts the south pole of another, and vice versa. Two north or two south poles repel each other. The names 'north' and 'south' reflect the fact that the Earth is a huge, very weak magnet. If you hang a magnet so that it can turn freely, its north pole will swing to face north. (So the North Pole of the Earth is a magnetic south pole!)

Since both electric currents and magnetism are caused by electrons moving, they interact, producing forces. A coil of wire produces a magnetic effect when an electric current flows through it. This is how an **electromagnet** – an electrically powered magnet – works. Moving a magnet near a coil of wire causes a current to flow in the coil. This is how a generator works. Passing an electric current through a wire near a magnet produces a force on the wire. This is how an electric motor works.